BUMPER
HOLIDAY
PUZZLE
BOOK

This is a Parragon book
This edition published in 2006

Parragon
Queen Street House
4 Queen Street
Bath BA1 1HE, UK

This edition © Parragon Books Ltd 2003
Individual puzzles Copyright © Puzzlemakers Ltd 2003
Cover courtesy of The Design House

This Book was created by Magpie Books,
an imprint of Constable & Robinson Ltd

ISBN 1-40547-100-X

Printed in India

A copy of the British Library Cataloguing-in-Publication
Date is available from the British Library

BUMPER HOLIDAY PUZZLE BOOK

p

1 Round the Block

You won't need a starting block to get you under way:
because it isn't a race!

Just arrange the 6-letter solutions to the clues into the six blocks
around each clue number.

Write the answers in a clockwise direction every time and you'll find
that the last answer fits into the first: the main problem will be to
decide in which square to put the first letter of each word...

1. Music disc
2. GP, for instance
3. Mythical beast

4. Average, standard
5. Beast
6. Plays, tragedies, etc

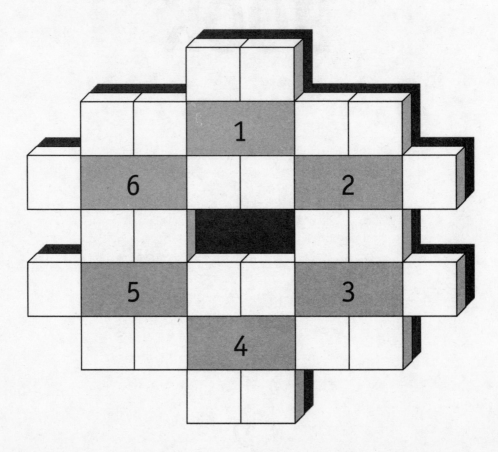

Coffee Break

Across

1. Viewpoint, belief (7)
5. Brittle transparent material (5)
8. A small piece of anything (7)
9. First letter of the Greek alphabet (5)
10. Fashion (5)
11. Garment worn by a priest (7)
12. Loath (6)
14. Go up (6)
17. Unable to relax or be still (7)
19. Sieves (5)
22. Brag (5)
23. Mischievous imp (7)
24. Correct, improve (5)
25. Of great force or power (7)

Down

1. Fertile tract in desert (5)
2. In a cold manner (5)
3. Have a strong impact on (7)
4. Observe (6)
5. Pasture (5)
6. Sanction (7)
7. Heaped (7)
12. Cordial (7)
13. Bring up (7)
15. Mistrust (7)
16. Plague (6)
18. Destined (5)
20. Criminal (5)
21. Relating to sound (5)

3 Codeword

Each number in the grid represents a different letter of the alphabet. You need to decipher the code and fill in the crossword. A checking grid is provided, which may be of help - and we've filled in three of the letters, to get you off to a good start...

A B C D E F G H I J K L M

N O P Q R S T U V W X Y Z

	17		18		4		20			3		22		26	
6	15	3	26	6	15	8	8		13	7	15	9	23	21	
	2		14		21		15		7		24		19		
6	9	26	18		14	15	23	21	9	8	26	19	26	18	
	23		26		4			23				8			
15	22	18	15	18	9	15	23		21	5	14	12	12	23	
			21		23		15				15		11		
20	9	1	9		22	9	19	26	23		14	4	26	20	
	23		19				26		9		25				
12	20	20	26	23	10		8	5	23	14	4	9	23	22	
	8				26				26		15		9		
3	26	23	3	7	15	8	9	3	21		23	15	16	26	
	2		26		18		23		26		10		6		
18	26	1	26	14	21		14	8	26	19	26	18	8	5	
	10		25		4		4		23		10		26		

1	2	3	4	5	6	7 U	8	9	10	11	12	13
14 C	15	16	17	18	19	20	21	22	23	24	25	26 E

4   *Phonetically Speaking* ABC

This mini quiz will test your knowledge of the international phonetic alphabet, where words are spelled with letters which are also words.

As an example, the word 'share' would be spelled out as:
Sierra, Hotel, Alpha, Romeo, Echo.

See how well you do with the following questions:

1. Which of these is the odd one out?
    Juliet Mike Oscar Victor Doris Charlie

2. Which month is found in the phonetic alphabet?

3. Which country can be found in the phonetic alphabet?

4. The capital of which country can be found in the phonetic alphabet?

5. Which Canadian province and city is found in the phonetic alphabet?

6. What type of clothing can be found in the phonetic alphabet?

7. Which family relative represents a letter in the phonetic alphabet?

8. Which popular game can be found in the phonetic alphabet?

9. Which dances are found in the phonetic alphabet?

10. Which unit of weight is found in the phonetic alphabet?

11. Which nymph who fell in love with Narcissus is found in the phonetic alphabet?

12. Which alcoholic beverage is found in the phonetic alphabet?

The vowels A, E, I, O and U have been removed from the crossword below. Can you replace them correctly? When you have, the first and last letters of every complete word containing an O can be rearranged to form another word.

	M		T			R		
S		P				O		N
S			R	S		N		L
		R						
D		T					R	
		H				N		S
	C			N		C		H
				T				
S		D	R		S	S		D

A A A A A

A A A A A

E E E E E E E E E

I I I O O

U U U U U

HIDDEN WORD: _____

6   *Couplets*

The grid below shows a central circle surrounded by shapes, linked to form six sets of three shapes apiece.

Can you place each of the two-letter groups, one per shape, so that every set of three (the central circle, plus the two matching shapes diagonally opposite one another) forms a six-letter word? Whichever pair of letters you place in the central circle will appear in the middle of every word.

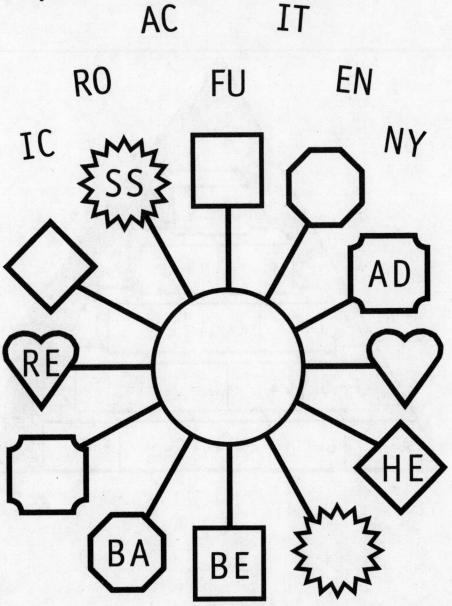

7   *Pyramid Plus*

Every brick in this pyramid contains a number which
is the sum of the two numbers below it, so that F=A+B, etc.
No two bricks contain the same number, or zero; and each of
the five bricks at the lowest level contains a different number.

Just work out the missing numbers!

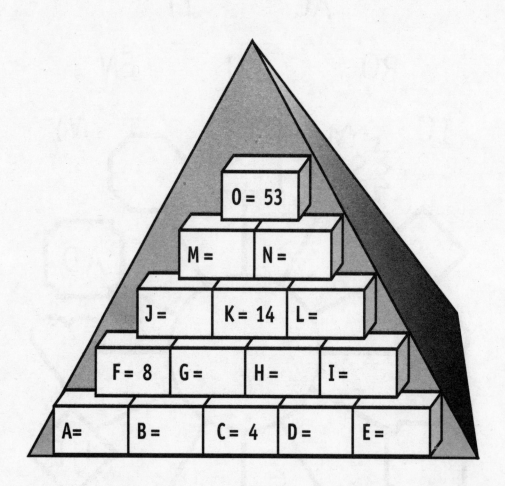

Mind Over Matter

Crack the mystery code to reveal the missing letter.
(Hint: The letters are valued 1-26 according to their
places in the alphabet.)

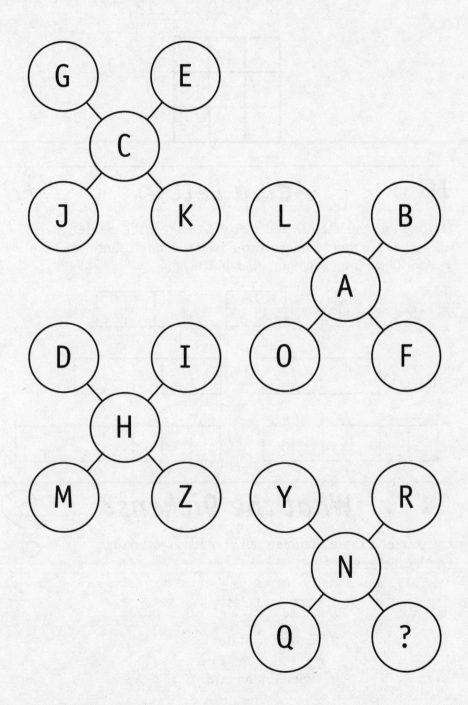

9 Magic Square

Fill the grid with these numbers, so that every row, column and the two long diagonals adds up to 27:

4 6 7 8 9 10 11 12 14

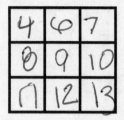

---

10 Add a Letter

A+B

Starting with the letter O, add a letter to make first a two-letter word, then another to make a three-letter word, etc, until you have a seven-letter word meaning: died under water.

| O |

| | |

| | | |

| | | |

| | | | |

| | | | | |

| | | | | | |

---

11 What the Dickens?

Can you solve these anagrams, all of which are works by Charles Dickens?

1. Harm a rot classic

2. To owe facilitates

3. Flipped video card

In-Words

Starting at the top left-hand corner, work your way to the centre of the grid. All the words overlap by either one or two letters - and a few have already been entered, to start you off...

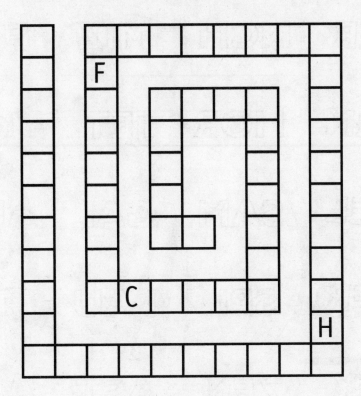

1. Liquid, dampness (8)
2. Draw back (6)
3. Ten-sided shape (7)
4. An attack or beginning (5)
5. Heavenly, spirit-like (8)
6. Restrict (5)
7. Causing irritation (7)
8. Laugh loudly (6)
9. Overwhelmed, humbled (9)
10. The seed of a nut (6)
11. Pass, expire (6)
12. More than one (7)
13. Sharp, watchful (5)

Half & Half

Pair off these groups of three letters to make ten six-letter nautical terms.

LER   NCH   MIZ   FUN

ERN   HOR   JET   ICE

NEL   SAM   GAL   RUD

DER   SPL   LAU   TIL

LEY   ZEN   AST   ANC

_____   _____

_____   _____

_____   _____

_____   _____

_____   _____

14 A Cut Above

This crossword has been cut into many pieces. Can you reassemble it? We've placed some, to give you a start.

Whatever Next?

Study the sequences of numbers below and see if you can discover what comes next in each case...

A.

②   6   12   20   30   42   **?**

B.

①   1   2   3   5   ·8   13   **?**

C.

3   3   5   4   4   3   5   5   4   3   **?**

D.

8   11   16   23   32   43   **?**

E.

1   2   2   4   8   12   96   108   **?**

F.

0   3   8   15   24   35   48   **?**

G.

31   28   31   30   31   30   31   **?**

H.

3	2	1	5	1	?
1	3	6	6	30	?

16   *Popagram*

When the numbered anagrams are solved, the letters in
the shaded column reveal the name of a well-known songstress.

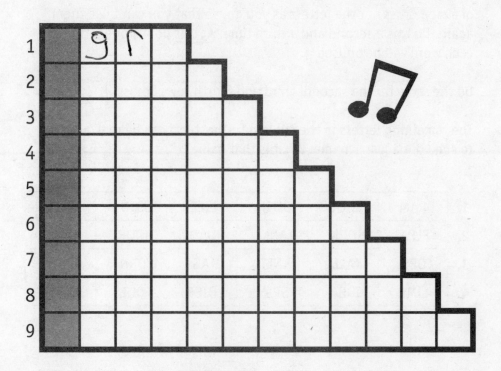

1. Gird

2. Blame

3. No kerb

4. Dial car

5. Mint mine

6. Cover a tax

7. I covet loom

8. Repulsed oak

9. Prepare doves

HIDDEN POP SINGER:_____

17 *Hidden Cities*

Twelve capital cities are hidden in the four-letter word groups. Starting with the first row across and working from left to right, take one letter from every word, to spell out the name of a city. Cross out the letters as you go, so that you can't use them again. Do this a second and a third time. At this point, one letter in each word will be unused.

Do the same for the second, third and fourth rows across.

The remaining letters in the column furthest left can be rearranged to spell out a man's name. What is that name?

1.	DRAM	BOUT	BUSH	LICE	COIN	NEWS
2.	PLEA	HORN	TANK	GOAD	HOUR	NAME
3.	COPS	TALE	KNIT	MAGI	WORN	GRAN
4.	LIMB	IDEA	SPIN	BIER	FOUL	NEAT

1. _____ _____ _____

2. _____ _____ _____

3. _____ _____ _____

4. _____ _____ _____

HIDDEN NAME: _____

Can you fit all of the listed words into the crossword below?

AMBER   BOOTLEG

CELLO   CANTEEN

CIVIC   CHICAGO

HAPPY   PHAETON

       ANGINA   ANAESTHETISED

       BISECT   ENVIRONMENTAL

       EXISTS   FLOODLIGHTING

       INDOOR   HANDKERCHIEFS

                     UNINHABITABLE

                     WATERPROOFING

19   *Summing Up*

$$
\begin{array}{r}
1 \\
+\ 2 \\
\times\ 3 \\
-\ 4 \\
\hline
5
\end{array}
$$

Arrange one of each of the numbers 3, 5, 6 and 8, as well as one of each of the symbols – (minus), x (times) and + (plus) in every row and column to arrive at the answer at the end of the row or column.

5	x	3	–	8	+	6	=	13
							=	25
							=	40
							=	46
=		=		=		=		
60		15		35		27		

---

20   *Real Names*

These people are better known by other names. What are the names by which they are more commonly recognised?

1. Harry Webb   _____

2. Marion Michael Morrison   _____

3. Doris Kappelhoff   _____

4. Edson Arantes do Nascimento   _____

5. Ruby Stevens   _____

6. Reginald Kenneth Dwight   _____

7. Kate Price   _____

8. Vincent Damon Furnier   _____

9. William Broad   _____

10. Demetria Guynes   _____

Fallen Tiles

The letters on the tiles were once all in place in the grid below, before they dropped out, falling in a straight, vertical line into the lower grid.

Some letter tiles dropped earlier than others, so those on the lowest row of the bottom grid aren't necessarily all from the same row in the grid above.

Can you replace all of the letter tiles and thus reveal a quotation attributed to Groucho Marx? Words may continue from one line to the next where necessary and the black squares indicate spaces between words.

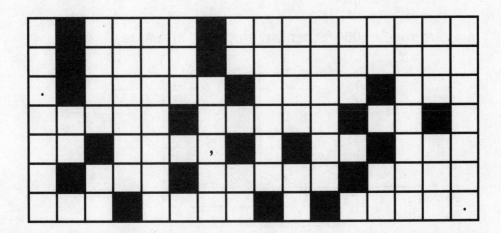

22 Logic Puzzle: A Moving Story

Five residents of Vendor View have just bought flats of different sizes, for different prices, in different towns. Can you discover the town to which each is moving and the price of his or her new home?

1. Deborah's flat didn't cost as much as the one in Ayr, which was purchased by Darren.

2. Keith isn't the person who has just bought a flat in Rugby, for £45,000.

3. The resident moving to Hayes paid £90,000 for a new flat in a purpose-built block.

4. Laura paid £70,000 for her flat, which isn't in Kendal.

	Moving to					Price paid				
	Ayr	Hayes	Kendal	Rhyll	Rugby	£35,000	£40,000	£45,000	£70,000	£90,000
Darren										
Deborah										
George										
Keith										
Laura										
£35,000											
£40,000											
£45,000											
£70,000											
£90,000											

Resident	Moving to	Price paid

23   *Roundword*

Write the answer to each clue in a clockwise direction.
Every solution overlaps the next by either one, two or three letters
and each solution starts in its numbered section. The solution to the
final clue ends with the letter in the first square.

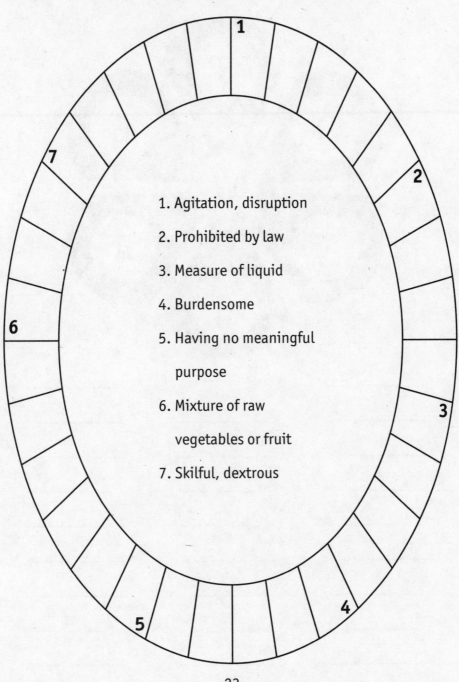

1. Agitation, disruption

2. Prohibited by law

3. Measure of liquid

4. Burdensome

5. Having no meaningful

   purpose

6. Mixture of raw

   vegetables or fruit

7. Skilful, dextrous

Flow-Words

How many words of three or more different letters can
you make from those on the petals, without using plurals,
abbreviations or proper nouns?
The central letter must appear in every word.

R

D

E

W

T

A

S

_____   _____   _____

_____   _____   _____

_____   _____   _____

_____   _____   _____

_____   _____   _____

_____   _____   _____

_____   _____   _____

25 *Jigsaw*

Fit the jigsaw together to reveal eight islands.

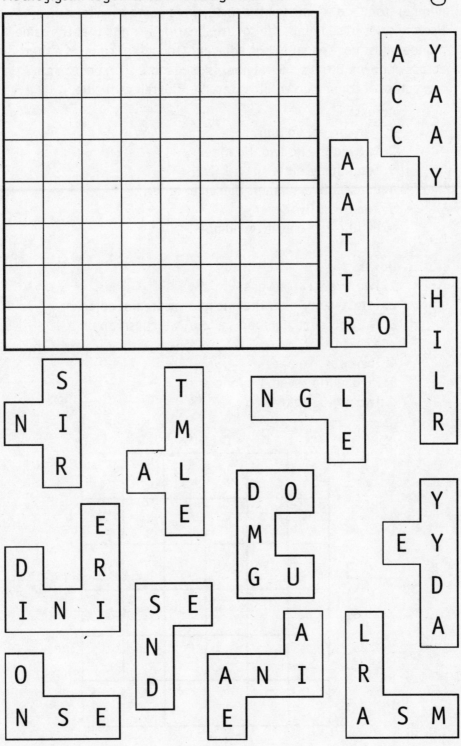

Figure It Out

Each of the thirty-six squares in the grid is filled with a single digit number from 1 to 9 - each of those numbers being used four times. Use the clues to complete the square, bearing in mind that the same number must not appear in two adjacent (touching) squares either across or down. If the same number is used more than once in any row across or column down, it is stated in the relevant clue.

Across:
1. Two threes. No four.
2. Two eights. No two. No nine.
3. Total thirty-nine.
4. Consecutive numbers placed in order.
5. Two twos. Two sevens.
6. Eight is the only even number.

Down:
1. Two sixes. Two sevens.
2. Total twenty-one. The one and six are not adjacent.
3. The only even number is a four, which isn't next to a seven.
4. Two twos. No one.
5. No one. No seven. No nine.
6. Two nines. No five.

	1	2	3	4	5	6
1						
2						
3						
4						
5						
6						

Coffee Break

Across

1. Disney fawn (5)
3. — and Sullivan (7)
6. Rectangles (7)
8. From India, for example (5)
10. Ornithologist (11)
12. Bucket (4)
13. Hellenic (5)
15. Scratch (4)
17. Attendees at Royal Albert Hall, perhaps (11)
19. Ahead of time (5)
20. Suntanned (7)
21. Reins (7)
22. Frown (5)

Down

1. Man of the cloth (6)
2. Latin American country (6)
3. Oxygen, for instance (3)
4. Primary (5)
5. Treeless, Arctic plain (6)
7. Lasting (8)
9. List of dates (8)
10. Game with numbered balls (5)
11. Stops (5)
14. Verbal address (6)
15. Humorously sarcastic (6)
16. German composer (6)
18. Fruit with sweet, juicy flesh (5)
20. Double-decker (3)

28   *Ring-Words*

From the thirty-two segments below, find sixteen 6-letter words, by pairing one set of three letters with another. All of the segments must be used once only.

RRY · EST · ONG · WIT · THM · SPH · HIN · STS · OWN · SOP · RHY · NYM · FUR · LOW · ING · THR · INS · ROW · SMO · HYS · TWI · FLU · THR · GHT · HOR · OOZ · INX · GGY · ROR · KNI · PHS · ULT

_____   _____

_____   _____   _____

_____   _____   _____

_____   _____   _____

_____   _____   _____

_____   _____   _____

29   *Spot the Difference*

Can you spot the seven differences between these two pictures?
Mark them in the lower picture.

Dog & Bone

Here's one for the children... help Douglas the dog to dig
his way down to the bone. There's only one way to go -
can you discover the way?

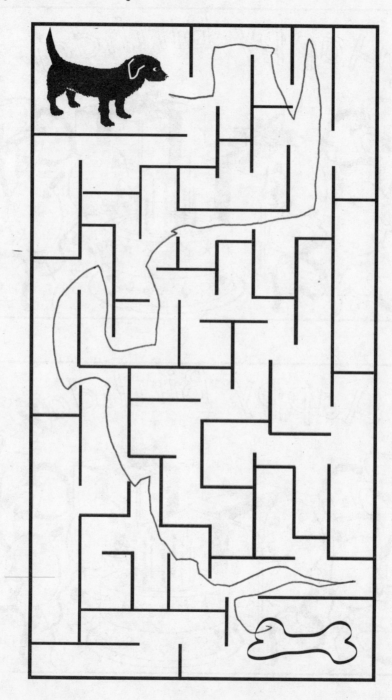

31 Shape Shifter

Each of the grids lettered A-E contains a shape fragment.
It is possible to construct more than one complete shape from every fragment, by filling in additional blocks. The clues will help you to discover the five correct shapes from the nine choices available.

Clues:

1. Grids B and D require the same number of blocks to be filled in.
2. Fill in more blocks in grid A than in grid D.
3. Fill in fewer blocks in grid C than in grid B.
4. Fill in more blocks in grid E than in grid A.

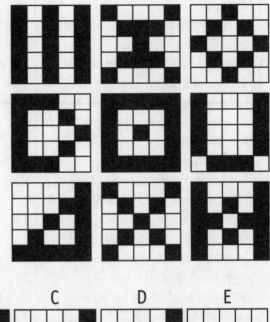

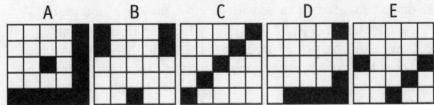

The number of additional blocks filled into each grid will correspond with two letters of the alphabet. From the decoding table below, write these two letters beneath each shape, in order, thus revealing something remarkable.

1 = LU	4 = OM	7 = PH	10 = OS
2 = DE	5 = AR	8 = ON	11 = EE
3 = SO	6 = EN	9 = QU	12 = TR

The Knowledge

General knowledge is the theme for this crossword...

Across

1. A number that divides into another exactly (6)
4. A mint-like plant attractive to felines (6)
9. — Doolittle appears in G B Shaw's *Pygmalion* (5)
10. The side of a coin bearing the principal symbol (7)
11. Cold-blooded vertebrate (7)
12. A raccoon-like mammal native to America (5)
13. Water channel between Greenland and Iceland (7,6)
15. Overarm swimming stroke (5)
16. Slender S African spear (7)
18. W Yorks city on River Aire (5)
20. Forename of Charles Darwin's physician grandfather (7)
21. Small square pasta cases with savoury filling (7)
22. Jargon of a particular group (5)
25. The subject of a brontophobe's fear (7)
27. The computer that picks premium bonds winners (5)
28. Title commonly given to William Shakespeare (3,4,2,4)
31. Prefix meaning extremely (5)
32. Italian port and city (7)
34. The level part of a staircase between flights (7)
35. Former UN Secretary-General, U — (5)
36. Two-player game where cards can be discarded for others (6)
37. Protein substance produced by

Down

1. A group of atoms containing one unpaired electron (4,7)
2. 18th-century British furniture-maker (11)
3. An inhabitant of Muscat, perhaps (5)
5. People who plead for causes or defendants (9)
6. The final transcendent goal of Buddhism (7)
7. The medical treatment of children (11)
8. The hundredth part of a Russian rouble (6)
14. Mythological giant with the world on his shoulders (5)
16. An artist's studio... (7)
17. ...and a wooden frame that may be found there (5)
19. A spirit in Muslim folklore and theology (5)
21. French stew of tomatoes and vegetables (11)
22. A bundle of papers, corn or 24 arrows (5)
23. Day of the year on which an event happened (11)
24. A blowfly with a brightly coloured body (11)
26. A writer of plays (9)
29. European country of which Tallinn is the capital (7)
30. — *For Living*; Noel Coward play (6)
33. Relating to ancient Rome (5)

Very Fishy

Two grids, but only one set of words. Can you discover which word fits into each grid? Where words are duplicated, put one into the upper fish grid and one into the lower fish grid.

BAIT
BASS
CARP
DACE
DACE
DORY
HAKE
LASK
REEL
REEL
TIDE

BREAM
NURSE
RINSE
RIVER
SKATE
TUNNY

MINNOW
SALMON
SCALES
SWIVEL
URCHIN
WADERS

GROUPER
HARBOUR
INSHORE
INSHORE
KEEPNET
MANATEE
SEAWEED

BAY
DAB
EEL
EEL
EFT
FRY
FRY
GUT
POD
RIG
RIG
ROD
ROE
SEA
SEA

What's it Worth?   ? x ? =

Each symbol stands for a different number. In order to reach the correct total at the end of each row and column, what is the value of a heart, club, diamond and spade?

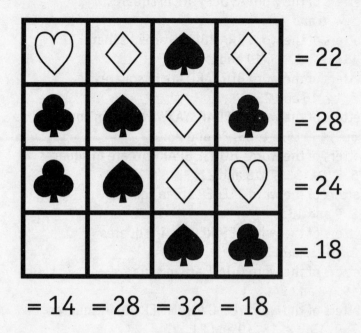

= 22
= 28
= 24
= 18

= 14   = 28   = 32   = 18

Each symbol stands for a different number. Given that these numbers are 1, 2, 3 and 6, how many circles are needed to balance scale C?

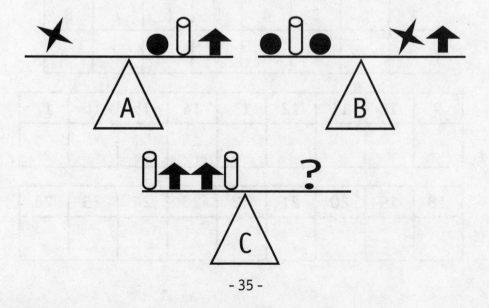

Place all twenty-six letters of the alphabet into the grid below, in such a way that:

1. The letters of the word AVOCET are in squares
   1, 2, 3, 4, 6 and 7.

2. The letters of the word BRAMBLING are in squares
   3, 9, 11, 12, 14, 15, 19 and 24.

3. The letters of the word BUZZARD are in squares
   3, 5, 9, 14, 16 and 23.

4. The letters of the words CEDAR WAXWING are in squares
   2, 3, 6, 9, 11, 15, 21, 23, 24 and 25.

5. The letters of the words HOUSE SPARROW are in squares
   2, 3, 5, 7, 9, 13, 17, 18 and 21.

6. The letters of the word JAEGER are in squares
   2, 3, 8, 9 and 15.

7. The letters of the word KESTREL are in squares
   2, 4, 9, 13, 19 and 20.

8. The letters of the word QUAIL are in squares
   3, 5, 19, 22 and 24.

9. The letters of the word YELLOWHAMMER are in squares
   2, 3, 7, 9, 10, 12, 18, 19 and 21.

Any unused letter is associated with any unused number.

A B C D E F G H I J K L M N O P Q R S T U V W X Y Z

1	2	3	4	5	6	7	8

9	10	11	12	13	14	15	16	17

18	19	20	21	22	23	24	25	26

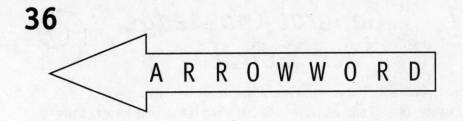

ARROWWORD

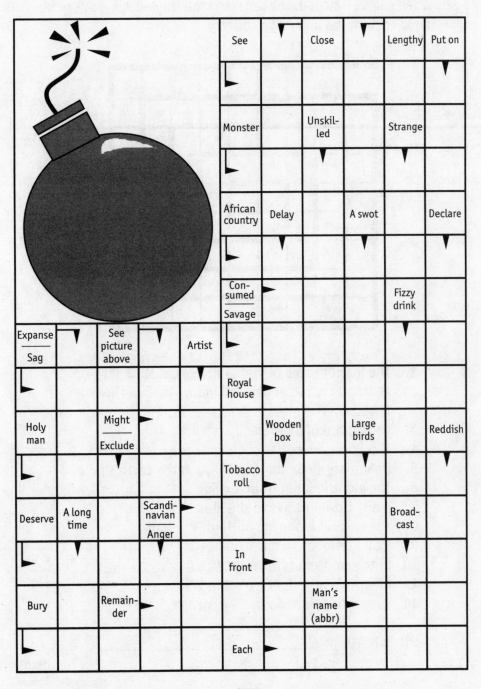

General Knowledge Spiral

Solve the clues in the normal way and enter them into the grid in a clockwise spiral. The last letter of each word is the first letter of the next. When you've finished, the letters in the shaded squares can be rearranged to form the name of a country.

1. The former name of Vietnam's Ho Chi Minh City
2. Mythical character who fell in love with his own reflection
3. The capital of Sweden
4. A double-size bottle of Champagne
5. Imaginary circle running through the Earth's poles
6. The eighth planet from the Sun
7. White flower native to the Alps
8. The ancient language of Hindus in India
9. Slang term for an old sixpence
10. Dutch painter of the *Night Watch*
11. America's president from 1945-53
12. A smooth-skinned variety of peach

HIDDEN WORD: _____

38 *Sidewords*

This puzzle can be solved in one of two ways, starting from either the top left corner or the bottom left corner. Can you find the two sequences of words?

Clues starting Top Left

1. Make possible (6)

2. A small fly (4)

3. Solid or determined (3)

4. Predilections (6)

5. A ringed planet (6)

6. Acid found in vinegar (6)

Clues starting Bottom Left

1. Refer to (4)

2. Metal container (3)

3. Furrow (3)

4. Material wealth (6)

5. Declare to be true (6)

6. Divine being (5)

7. A source of misery (4)

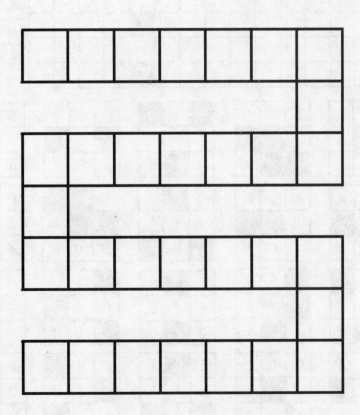

39   A Cut Above

This crossword has been cut into many pieces. Can you reassemble it? We've placed some, to give you a start.

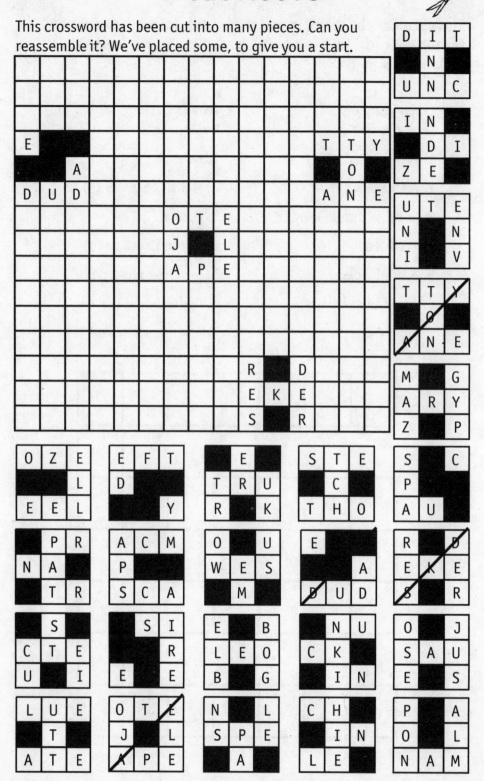

Missing Person

Hidden amongst the letters in the grid below is the name of a famous person from history. The letters of his name can be found reading either backwards or forwards, diagonally, vertically or horizontally, in a straight, uninterrupted line. Who is he?

D	C	L	A	U	J	P	O	T	Y	S	S
D	T	Q	A	C	V	M	H	G	F	A	P
I	S	X	Y	V	S	P	I	W	B	D	F
S	O	T	M	W	F	W	C	A	L	I	U
R	G	K	Q	X	R	Y	L	L	R	E	
A	H	G	S	D	E	W	C	V	L	B	G
E	J	X	Z	I	L	E	R	J	E	O	L
L	U	B	V	F	A	C	S	B	W	G	Y
X	Z	P	R	L	N	Y	T	Q	M	V	I
R	O	U	G	S	C	R	C	E	O	K	T
C	P	I	K	B	J	F	G	D	R	O	L
U	J	B	C	F	K	O	I	T	C	P	V
T	G	H	C	E	S	L	F	I	R	B	I
A	M	D	K	B	R	Q	S	T	E	F	S
L	I	S	A	V	A	L	X	Z	V	P	K
U	Y	B	Q	O	L	C	J	S	I	T	R
L	V	B	L	K	E	F	G	W	L	P	M
D	R	T	A	C	V	Z	X	I	O	Q	J
F	P	O	S	M	O	T	J	D	E	C	O

41   *Dice-Section*

Printed onto every one of the six numbered dice
seen stacked below are six letters (one per side), which
can be rearranged to form the answer to the clue for each die.
The problem is, you can only see three sides of any die! Use the
clues to solve the six-letter answers, writing them into the grid.
When correctly filled, the highlighted letters in the grid, read in
the order 1-6, will spell out another word, meaning: an allocation of
money.

1. Russian coin
2. Twosome
3. Tear in stocking
4. Unit of temperature
5. Light wind
6. More obese

1.
2.
3.
4.
5.
6.

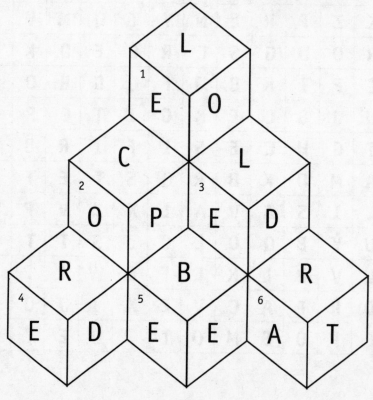

Round Tour

The answers to this puzzle form a continuous chain, starting at the top left-hand corner and following the direction indicated by the arrows. The last letter of each word is the first letter of the next and each clue is an anagram of its single-word solution. When completed correctly, the shaded squares contain letters which can be rearranged to spell out a mode of transport.

Take care with this one, as sometimes it is possible to form more than one word from the letters in the clue.

1. March

2. Dame

3. Red seat

4. Let row

5. Pool

6. No stamp

7. Thorn

8. Hour bar

9. Or sore chin

10. Least

11. Peals

12. Horse

13. Dieted

Start

Transport: _____

Cryptic Crossword

Across

1. This snake is a firm supporter (5)
4. Map religious pictures, perhaps (5)
7. Almost opening notebook ahead of time (6)
8. Look after hothead with a ring (4)
10. Object about verruca; it's frustrating (9)
11. Lamenting disrupted order (9)
14. Terrorists question a country (4)
15. Weak complaint written up by the French (6)
16. Eminent number reduced by little Theodore (5)
17. Equipment and plunder up on top shelf (5)

Down

1. Comfort star during cooked onion act (11)
2. Baste round an animal (5)
3. Permitting everyone's debts? (8)
5. These can be counted upon (5)
6. Inconsiderate hogs shuttle around (11)
9. Most concise cheese celebration? (8)
12. Sleep in it, but it's not right (5)
13. Forbidden graduate turned in as well (5)

Box Clever

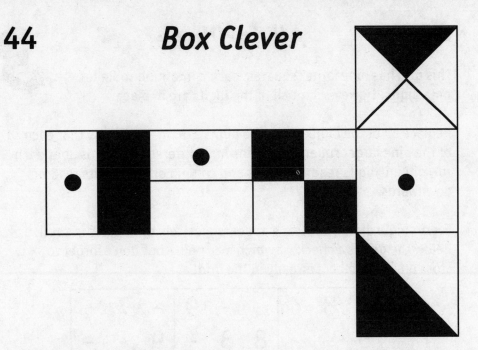

When the above is folded to form a cube, just one of the following can be produced. Which one?

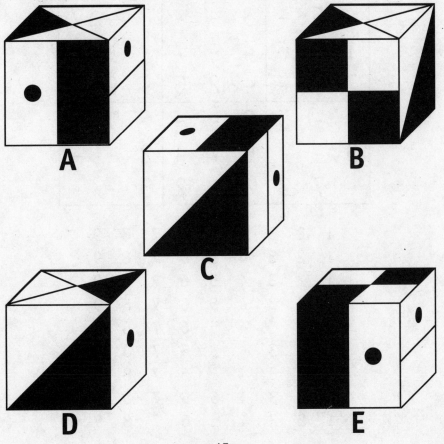

A

B

C

D

E

45   All in Place?

This grid has nine larger squares, each containing room for nine digits. However, not all of the digits are in place.

Replace all of the blanks with the digits 1-9, in such a way that each of the nine larger squares contains nine different digits, as does each row of nine digits reading across and column of nine digits reading downwards.

Every single digit from 1 to 9 appears precisely nine times in total. Below the grid is a checklist which may help - but don't forget to cross off the numbers already in the grid!

-	8	4	-	-	9	-	7	-
5	-	-	8	3	-	9	-	-
-	6	-	-	5	-	-	3	8
-	5	-	3	-	-	8	-	7
1	-	6	4	-	7	-	-	2
7	-	-	-	2	5	-	9	-
-	-	5	9	-	-	-	1	3
9	-	-	5	7	-	2	-	-
-	7	3	-	-	2	5	-	-

1 2 3 4 5 6 7 8 9
1 2 3 4 5 6 7 8 9
1 2 3 4 5 6 7 8 9
1 2 3 4 5 6 7 8 9
1 2 3 4 5 6 7 8 9
1 2 3 4 5 6 7 8 9
1 2 3 4 5 6 7 8 9
1 2 3 4 5 6 7 8 9
1 2 3 4 5 6 7 8 9

46   *Bermuda Triangle*

Travel through the 'Bermuda Triangle' by visiting one room at a time and collecting a letter from each. You can enter the outside passageway as often as you like, but can only visit each room once. When you've completed your tour, rearrange the fifteen letters to spell out a word.

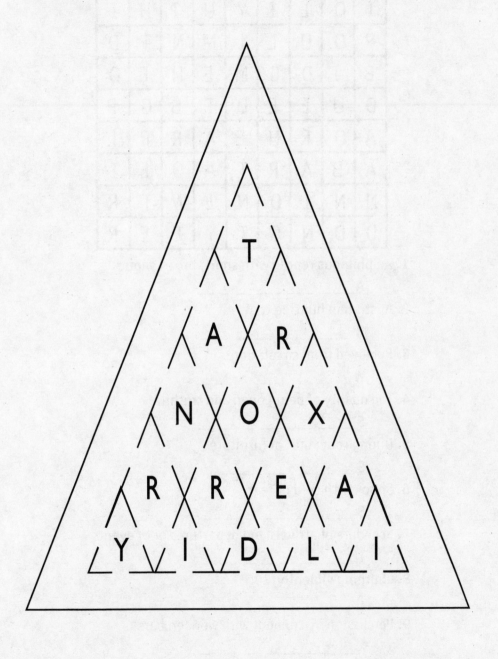

47 Downwords

The solutions to the clues are all nine-letter words, the letters for which are contained in the grid below, at the rate of one per line in the correct order. Every letter is used once only.

A	B	W	S	S	S	T	T	X
I	O	L	I	Y	U	I	H	I
R	O	U	L	L	M	N	T	D
B	I	D	C	M	E	H	E	O
D	U	E	E	D	T	B	G	P
A	O	R	H	E	A	R	R	L
A	B	A	R	T	A	O	E	I
N	N	L	O	N	E	W	T	R
D	D	N	G	T	Y	E	E	R

1. Amphibious reptile with short, broad snout

A _ _ _ _ _ _ _ _

2. Australian hunting tool

B _ _ _ _ _ _ _ _

3. Removed from circulation

W _ _ _ _ _ _ _ _

4. The quality of being open and truthful

S _ _ _ _ _ _ _ _

5. Dining room unit of furniture

S _ _ _ _ _ _ _ _

6. Shook with cold or fear

S _ _ _ _ _ _ _ _

7. Schedule of arrivals and departures or of events

T _ _ _ _ _ _ _ _

8. Churning violently

T _ _ _ _ _ _ _ _

9. Percussion instrument with wooden bars

X _ _ _ _ _ _ _ _

Coffee Break

Across

1. Black and white animal (5)
3. Caustic (7)
6. Sports competitor (7)
8. Let up (5)
10. Lacking distinguishing characteristics (11)
12. Piece of grass (4)
13. Implied (5)
15. Give up (4)
17. Site of conflict (11)
19. Congest (5)
20. Make sound by pursing lips (7)
21. Appearance of a place (7)
22. Scent (5)

Down

1. Partisan (6)
2. Alleviation (6)
3. First-rate (3)
4. Insurgent (5)
5. Dairy product (6)
7. Worn to shreds (8)
9. Flourish (8)
10. Rime (5)
11. Strayed (5)
14. Calculating machine (6)
15. Nearer (6)
16. Skin problem (6)
18. Souvenir (5)
20. Means (3)

Magic Squares

Use every letter to the side of each grid to fill the crossword completely, in such a way that each crossword reads the same across as down. For each crossword, three letters have been given as a start...

L	L			
L				

A A A A A
B B E E E
E E I L L
L̶ L̶ L̶ M M
R R T T T

A A C D
D D D E E
E E G G I
I N N O O
R̶ R̶ R̶ R R

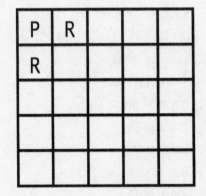

P	R			
R				

50   *Cards on the Table*

What is the face value and suit of each of the cards shown below? Together they total 87. All twelve cards are of different values. In the pack, the values of the cards are as per their numbers and ace = 1, jack = 11, queen = 12 and king = 13. No card is horizontally or vertically next to another of the same colour (hearts and diamonds are red; spades and clubs are black) and there are four different suits in every horizontal row and three different suits in each vertical column.

1. The value of card C is one lower than that of card H, which has a value two lower than the value of card F.
2. The king of clubs is directly above the queen of hearts, which isn't horizontally next to a spade.
3. Card D has an even-numbered value.
4. The card with a value of one is either E, F, G or H.
5. Card L is a diamond. The jack is not a diamond.
6. The three is horizontally next to a card with a value one lower than that of card I.
7. The value of card A is equal to the total value of cards I, J and K.

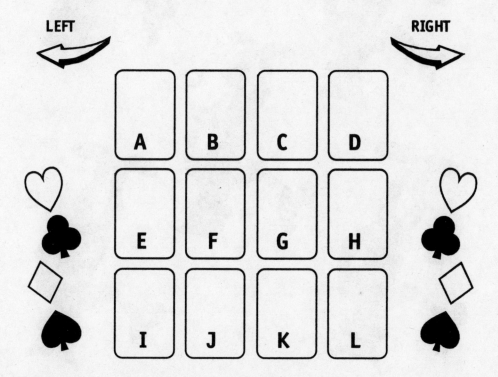

51 *Shadowman*

Test your skills of observation.
Only one of the five shadows
is that of the man waving his
handkerchief. Which one?

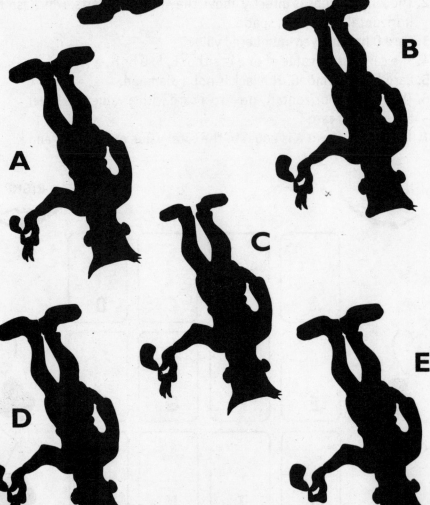

52   *Word Ladders*

Lewis Carroll is widely credited with the invention of the Word Ladder puzzle, the first appearing in *Vanity Fair* on 29 March, 1879. In this puzzle, you need to change one word into another, by altering one letter at a time. However, the positions of each letter must remain unchanged.

Here's an example, changing the word TEA to POT:

T	E	A
P	E	A
P	E	T
P	O	T

Now solve these:

P	I	G
S	T	Y

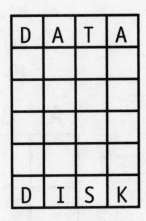

D	A	T	A
D	I	S	K

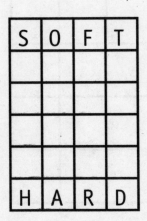

S	O	F	T
H	A	R	D

R	E	A	D
B	O	O	K

53   *Sum Square*   **+ - x**

The grid should be filled with numbers from 1 to 6, so that each number appears just once in each row and column. The clues refer to the digit totals in the squares, eg A 1 2 3 = 11 means that the numbers in squares A1, A2 and A3 add up to 11.

1. A 1 2 3 = 11
2. A B C 6 = 14
3. A B 1 = 11
4. B 3 4 = 3
5. B C 6 = 11
6. C D E 4 = 8
7. D 1 2 = 4
8. D E 5 = 8
9. E F 4 = 8
10. F 1 2 = 10

	A	B	C	D	E	F
1						
2						
3						
4						
5						
6						

54 *Skeleton*

Given just three clue numbers and three black squares, can you solve this crossword? When the puzzle is complete, the pattern of the black squares will be symmetrical.

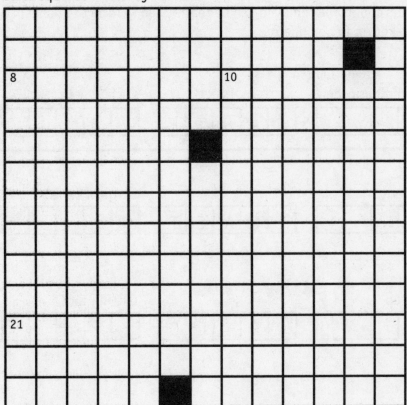

Across

1. Garbage
5. Compact or stupid
8. Seasonal song
9. Style, flair
11. Cowboy exhibitions
13. Lifeless or infertile
14. Volatile, moody
16. Lessen
18. Quick and agile
21. Put to death
23. Odour or fragrance
24. Toy bear
25. Late

Down

1. Happen again
2. Tedium, ennui
3. Eskimo's dwelling
4. Leap on one leg
6. More agreeable
7. Everlasting
10. The white of an egg
12. Snake
14. Suffering
15. Small-format newspaper
17. Great fear
19. Fatuous
20. Escape from
22. The self

55   *Give & Take*

Solve the clues on the left by removing a letter from the central word and rearranging the rest. Do the same for the clues on the right, only this time by adding a letter. When you've finished, the ten letters added and removed can be rearranged to form the name of a well-known TV personality.

A religious order

C	A	S	T	E

Coffin

Orderly

E	N	A	C	T

Surgical knife

Get up

C	R	I	E	S

Cutting tool

A small residue

R	I	D	G	E

Waist-belt

In case

T	A	L	E	S

Unchanging

HIDDEN TV PERSONALITY:_____

56 *Flow-Words*

How many words of three or more different letters can you make from those on the petals, without using plurals, abbreviations or proper nouns?
The central letter must appear in every word.

I

P   Y

A

M   F

L

_____   _____   _____

_____   _____   _____

_____   _____   _____

_____   _____   _____

_____   _____   _____

_____   _____   _____

_____   _____   _____

_____   _____   _____

57   *Figure of Eight*

Solve the clues and enter the answers in the correspondingly numbered squares. The first letter of each word should be entered immediately above the number and the words can read in either a clockwise or anticlockwise direction. A number of letters have already been entered, to start you on your way.

1. Almond-flavoured biscuit
2. Briskness
3. Deprive of mobility or freedom to move
4. Produce, bring into existence
5. Raw vegetables cut into bite-sized strips and served with a dip
6. Close and intense examination
7. Start or set in motion
8. Small talk, gossip
9. Not growing or changing; without force or vitality
10. Lacking knowledge
11. Protector, often of a child
12. Shakespearean sorcerer, father of Miranda in *The Tempest*
13. Implements of war, armaments
14. A decorative object
15. Pleasing in appearance, good-looking
16. The product of a body's mass and its velocity, impetus
17. Without pity
18. Legendary Greek hero; when he was a baby his mother tried to make him immortal by bathing him in a magical river but the heel by which she held him remained vulnerable
19. Exaggerated masculine pride
20. Rare, not ordinarily encountered
21. The highest point, the highest level or degree attainable
22. Select, propose as a candidate for some honour
23. Various, of many different kinds purposefully arranged but lacking any uniformity

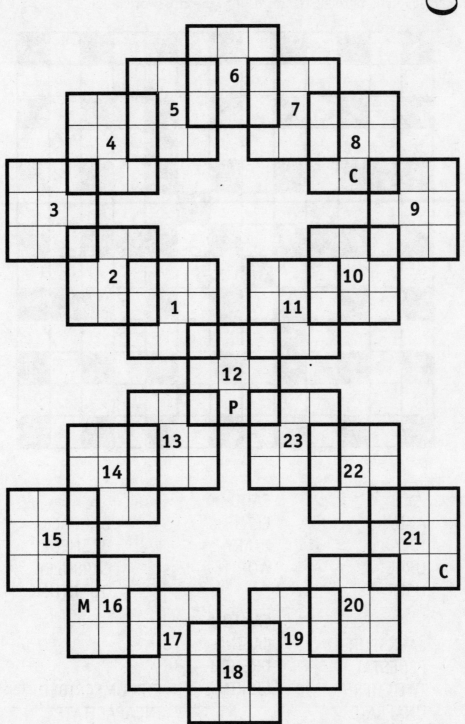

Filling-in Time

Can you fit all of the listed words into the crossword below?

ANEW	CADDY
IDEA	CLIMB
URGE	DIARY
USER	WORTH

	BARRACK
	BASHFUL
	CAPSULE
	QUANTUM

LARKSPUR	CANTON
PEDESTAL	CASINO
TWITCHER	DRENCH
UNAFRAID	SISKIN

CIRCUMSCRIBED

INCAPACITATED

59   *Crack-It*

Use the alphanumeric references to connect the dots horizontally. All of the required horizontal lines are listed.

Look at the available shapes, to work out which of the remaining dots you need to connect with vertical lines; and (if available) use the central connection ring to create any required diagonals.

When you have matched six of the eight shapes, take the value of each (given above the shape) and complete the arithmetical progression to find the value of S.

Horizontal references:

1.   A B C   D E F

        G H I   J K L

2.   M N O

3.   A B C   G H I   P Q R

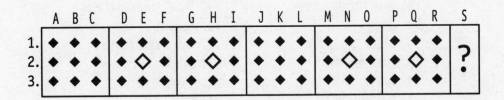

Around the Squares

The answer to each clue is a four-letter word, to be entered in the four squares surrounding the corresponding number in the grid. The word can start in any of the four squares and read either clockwise or anticlockwise. The first has already been entered, to get you started.

	L						
0	1 D	2	3	4	5	6	
	G						
	7	8	9	10	11	12	
	13	14	15	16	17	18	
	19	20	21	22	23	24	
	25	26	27	28	29	30	
	31	32	33	34	35	36	

1. Precious metal
2. Not light
3. Clawed sea-creature
4. Splash of ink
5. Owl's cry
6. Job
7. Radiate
8. Not at home
9. Remain
10. Jog
11. Pond
12. Run tongue over
13. Seep
14. Skull
15. Uttered
16. Track
17. Devious plan
18. Gash
19. Labyrinth
20. Despise
21. Not working
22. Notion
23. Farm animal
24. Chant
25. Repast
26. Inform
27. Country road
28. Stingy
29. Water-filled ditch
30. Title, nomenclature
31. As well
32. Brick structure
33. Duck's feathers
34. Daybreak
35. Timber
36. Relocate

Hexagony

Can you place the hexagons into the grid, so that where any triangle touches another along a straight line, the letter in both triangles is the same? No rotation of any hexagon is allowed!

Codeword

Each number in the grid represents a different letter of the alphabet. You need to decipher the code and fill in the crossword. A checking grid is provided, which may be of help - and we've filled in three of the letters, to get you off to a good start...

A B C D E F G H I J K L M

N O P Q R S T U V W X Y Z

21	7	21	18	9	21		6	21	1	26	17	26	5	13
10			21		1		24		26		24		6	
22	8	2	13	26	12	2	9		23	26	8	18	9	13
18			16		2		23		9		5		1	
9	15	6	9	24	26	10	9	14	13		13	25	26	14
		9			9		14				22		21	
21	22	21	1	2	5		13	9	24	24	26	22	18	9
	8		9		1				9		13		18	
21	4	19	21	1	9	14	13		13	26	9	4	20	9
	20		5				9		9			2		
8	3	24	9		1	16	21	26	14	5	10	8	11	9
	2		17		21		24		13		21			1
19	21	25	26	14	3		8	24	26	3	26	14	21	18
	24		24		9		8		23		7			21
21	4	4	9	14	4	2	10		9	15	9	10	6	13

1	2	3	4	5	6	7 Z	8	9	10	11	12	13
14 N	15	16	17	18	19	20	21	22	23	24	25	26 I

63 *Ring-Words*

From the thirty-two segments below, find sixteen 6-letter words, by pairing one set of three letters with another. All of the segments must be used once only.

Ring segments (from outer to inner):

- IKH
- INE
- ZLE
- GOV
- BAD
- GER
- TLE
- PLE
- RHY
- PPY
- SKY
- THE
- SOO
- CLO
- EXH
- FRI
- WIM
- LUX
- ELI
- SHE
- MES
- ORT
- WOO
- INF
- SER
- GUZ
- DED
- XIR
- CHO
- ERN
- HUR
- SHR

Which figure below continues the sequence above?

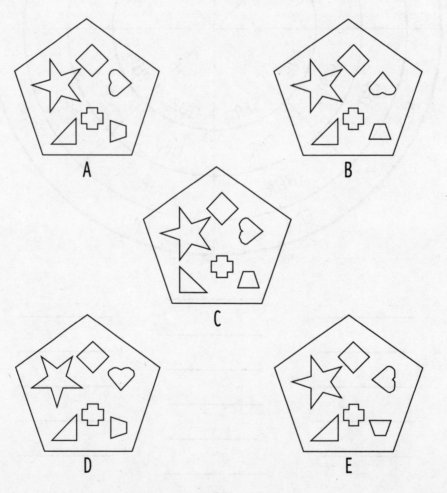

Vowel Movements

The vowels A, E, I, O and U have been removed from the crossword below. Can you replace them correctly? When you have, the first and last letters of every complete word containing an O can be rearranged to form another word.

	N		L		G		S	T
R	■		■	V				■
	S	R			L		T	
S	■		■	R			■	■
		R	T	H			S	T
■		■			L			
	G		M		N			C
■		■	R		T	■		
G	R		D				S	T

A A A A A A A A

E E E E E E E E E E

I I I I I I I

O O

U U

HIDDEN WORD: _____

66 Couplets

The grid below shows a central circle surrounded by shapes, linked to form six sets of three shapes apiece.

Can you place each of the two-letter groups, one per shape, so that every set of three (the central circle, plus the two matching shapes diagonally opposite one another) forms a six-letter word? Whichever pair of letters you place in the central circle will appear in the middle of every word.

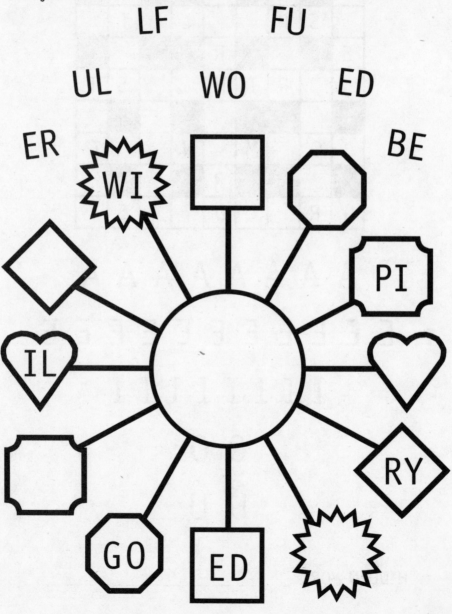

Alphanumerical

In this puzzle the numbers from 1 to 26 have been replaced by different letters of the alphabet. The sums below will enable you to crack the code. NB - The only arithmetical signs used in this puzzle are '+' (plus), '-' (minus) and 'x' (times).

1. $B \times B = I$
2. $I \times I = Y$
3. $J - M = O$
4. $W \times Q = T$
5. $V + I = X$
6. $W \times W = Z$
7. $K + A = G$
8. $N - D = Q$

9. $(F + F) \times O = P$
10. $Q \times Q = C$
11. $K + E = L$
12. $E + S = R$
13. $(M \times M) - (I \times I) = R$
14. $I + I = U$
15. $H + B = C$
16. $U + K = J$

A	B	C	D	E	F	G	H	I	J	K	L	M

N	O	P	Q	R	S	T	U	V	W	X	Y	Z

1	2	3	4	5	6	7	8	9	10	11	12	13

14	15	16	17	18	19	20	21	22	23	24	25	26

68 *Double-Crosser*

Two crossword puzzles - but you have to decide which solution fits into each crossword. In both cases, one word has been entered, to give you a start!

1		2		3		4		5		6
				7						
8						9				
				10 N	E	E				
11	12		13			14	15		16	
17		18		19		20		21		22
				23						
24						25				
				26						
27						28				

Across

1. Herb; Christmas song (5)
4. Capital of Egypt; Induce (5)
7. Bustle; By way of (3)
8. Intermission; Ball game (5)
9. Decoration; Juicy fruit (5)
10. Social insect; Named prior to marriage (3)
11. Foe; Correct (5)
14. Big; Delicacy (5)
17. Cutting weapon; Dissuade (5)
20. Proficient; Stomach (5)
23. Anger; Regret (3)
24. Military vehicles; Eskimo hut (5)
25. Junk; Wash off soap (5)
26. Sign of the zodiac; Vocal pitch (3)
27. Rush; Relating to sea waves (5)
28. Glaringly vivid; Pear juice drink (5)

Double-Crosser

Down

1. Cut thinly; Very thin candle (5)
2. Immature; Rascal (5)
3. Special occasion; Place for temporary parking (5)
4. Celestial body; Desert animal (5)
5. Waster; Not justified (5)
6. Acclaim; Unit of weight (5)
12. Novel; Frozen water (3)
13. Impair; Garden tool (3)
15. Reverence; Colour (3)
16. Mousse; Snake (3)
17. Canonised person; From the Netherlands (5)
18. Lubricated; Adult male singing voice (5)
19. Hazardous; Comical in a whimsical way (5)
20. Mineral; Greek tale teller (5)
21. Ocean-going vessel; Mistake (5)
22. Slang for 'drunk'; Give up (5)

69 *Logic Puzzle: Book Reviews*

Paige Turner is a book reviewer for one of the Sunday supplements. Each month she reviews five books and gives them a different star rating. This month's selection includes a few very unusual novels by up-and-coming authors. Can you match each author with the title of his or her book and the number of stars each was awarded?

1. *Heaven Sent*, which received five stars (Paige's highest award), wasn't written by Geoff Bowler.
2. Clive Kent's novel received either two or three fewer stars than that penned by Cindy Ross. Either Cindy Ross wrote *Wishing Well* or she wrote the book that received four stars - not both!
3. The book written by Louise Jameson (not entitled *Danger Money*) received at least two fewer stars than *Milestone*, which wasn't written by Cindy Ross.
4. Geoff Bowler's book received one more star than *Danger Money*.

	Danger Money	Heaven Sent	High Life	Milestone	Wishing Well	1	2	3	4	5
Cindy Ross										
Clive Kent										
Geoff Bowler										
Louise Jameson										
Margot Price										
1 star					
2 stars					
3 stars					
4 stars					
5 stars					

Book Title / No of stars

Author	Title	No of stars

Domino Placement

A standard set of 28 dominoes has been laid out as shown. Can you draw in the edges of them all? We've placed one to give you a start and the check-box is provided as an aid.

```
                5   4
            5   3   6   0
            6   0   6   2
    6   2   1   5   5   1   2   5
4   0   3   1   1   6   5   2   0   4
4   6   5   2   0   0   0   2   4   1
    3   5   1   1   4   1   3   3
            3   6   6   2
            3   4   4   3
                0   2
```

0-0	0-1	0-2	0-3	0-4	0-5	0-6

1-1	1-2	1-3	1-4	1-5	1-6	2-2

2-3	2-4	2-5	2-6	3-3	3-4	3-5

3-6	4-4	4-5	4-6	5-5	5-6	6-6

Figure It Out

Each of the thirty-six squares in the grid is filled with a single digit number from 1 to 9 - each of those numbers being used four times. Use the clues to complete the square, bearing in mind that the same number must not appear in two adjacent (touching) squares either across or down. If the same number is used more than once in any row across or column down, it is stated in the relevant clue.

Across:
1. Total twenty-one.
2. Total thirty-nine.
3. Consecutive numbers placed in order.
4. The highest and lowest digits are adjacent.
5. Two nines.
6. Total twenty-one.

Down:
1. Two nines. Two is the lowest number.
2. Consecutive numbers placed in order.
3. Two threes. Total twenty-one.
4. Two eights. No four.
5. Two sixes. Total forty.
6. No seven.

	1	2	3	4	5	6
1						
2						
3						
4						
5						
6						

Back and Forth

This one will take a bit of thinking about... The solutions to the Across clues should be entered into the grid in the traditional way, but those to the Down clues should be entered upside down. We've filled in the first, as an example.

Across
1. Verse (5)
4. Soup serving spoon (5)
7. Deteriorated (11)
8. Biblical man (3)
9. Spire (7)
11. Nonsynthetic (7)
14. Bounder (3)
16. Low-spirited (11)
17. Steam bath (5)
18. Border (5)

Down
1. Duck with soft, fine down (5)
2. Inadvertently (11)
3. Scorch (5)
4. Recruit (5)
5. Looked forward to (11)
6. Give qualities or abilities to (5)
10. Social insect (3)
11. A closed litter for one passenger (5)
12. Find repugnant (5)
13. Fragile (5)
15. Finished (5)

Round Tour

The answers to this puzzle form a continuous chain, starting at the top left-hand corner and following the direction indicated by the arrows. The last letter of each word is the first letter of the next and some have already been entered to get you started. When complete, the letters along the shaded row will reveal the name of a well-known film director.

1. Quadrilateral with two parallel sides (9)
2. Brick-bonding substance (6)
3. Uncommunicativeness (9)
4. Bird of prey with bald and golden varieties (5)
5. Cream-filled cake (6)
6. Murder of a king (8)
7. Number of players in a cricket team (6)
8. Usual state of affairs (9)
9. Muslim woman's veil (7)
10. Loud horn (6)
11. Great in quantity (8)
12. Breathing apparatus (7)
13. Complicated network of passages (9)
14. Abode (10)
15. Recent arrival (8)
16. Morally just (9)
17. Ancient Japanese warrior (7)
18. False perception (8)
19. Guide or helmsman (9)
20. German measles (7)
21. Light silvery metal (9)
22. Atlantic island (7)
23. Someone who works to abolish law and government (9)
24. Statement made under oath (9)
25. Slang term for an American (6)

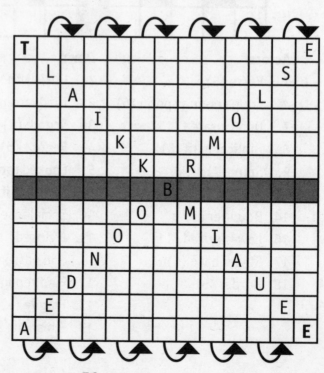

In-Words

Starting at the top left-hand corner, work your way to the centre of the grid. All the words overlap by either one or two letters - and a few have already been entered, to start you off...

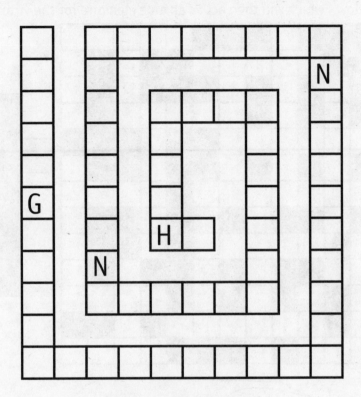

1. Introduction to a play (8)
2. The select few (5)
3. Dogged or stubborn (9)
4. Practical, handy (6)
5. Mock with satire (7)
6. One who observes (8)
7. A short trip or task (6)
8. Slow learner or simpleton (5)
9. Blame, rebuke (7)
10. Enter one's name (8)
11. Extremist, revolutionary (7)
12. Set down (6)

In the Name of...

Mr & Mrs Wordsmith are having their baby daughter Christened this afternoon, but it may take quite some time, since they've given their child no fewer than 25 forenames. Please enter them all into the grid below - which will then act as an aide memoire for the vicar!

I name this child:

AMY	HILARY
ANNE	INGRID
ARIADNE	LEE
BELINDA	MARY
DEIRDRE	MURIEL
DELLA	ROSIE
DIANE	RUBY
DOREEN	SYLVIA
ELAINE	TANYA
EMMA	TINA
ERICA	VERA
GERI	WENDY
	YOLANDE

76 *Animal Tracks*

Move through the grid from letter to adjacent letter, in any direction except diagonally, in order to track down the hidden animals. All of the letters must be used, but none more than once.

G	I	E	E	R	C	N	I	E	K
A	R	R	D	O	C	G	U	Y	N
F	F	L	F	D	O	N	E	B	O
H	E	I	L	I	L	R	P	I	M
I	P	Z	O	W	E	E	H	S	L
O	P	A	R	X	L	N	T	O	E
P	E	L	D	N	Y	A	P	N	M
O	S	E	P	A	R	D	N	C	A
T	U	P	O	E	L	T	O	I	L
A	M	H	A	N	T	I	G	E	R

Coffee Break

Across

1. Fail to meet financial obligation (7)
5. Accolade (5)
8. Shoemaker (7)
9. Implores (5)
10. Panorama (5)
11. Gap (7)
12. Wallops (6)
14. Soars upwards (6)
17. Liquidiser (7)
19. Very fast (5)
22. Alert (5)
23. Cleanliness (7)
24. Upright (5)
25. Went around (7)

Down

1. Wharves (5)
2. Legend (5)
3. Most unsightly (7)
4. Overwhelming fear (6)
5. Plenty (5)
6. Astounding (7)
7. Patterns (7)
12. Garden vegetable (7)
13. Control (7)
15. Vertical (7)
16. Legendary king of the Britons (6)
18. Inhabited (5)
20. Pressed fold (5)
21. Apprehension (5)

Extensowords

w-o-r-d-s

The beginning of each word in this grid is a word in itself, separately clued. When the puzzle is completed, the letters in the shaded vertical column will reveal the title of a 1990 film.

1.
2.
3.
4.
5.
6.
7.
8.
9.
10.
11.
12.

	START WORD	WHOLE WORD
1.	Greater quantity	Dark red cherry
2.	Cease, conclude	Support or approve
3.	Watery vapour	Error of judgment
4.	Rigid support	An inspired teacher
5.	Pig meat	Hanging bed
6.	South African warriors	Lacking reverence
7.	Eat or drink	Highest or best
8.	Shipboard prison cell	Body of troops
9.	Before	Constructed
10.	Young sheep	Latin American dance
11.	Throw	Campaigning groups
12.	Grand, heroic	Connoisseur of food

FILM TITLE: _____

Tiles

In these puzzles, the tiles must be fitted into the pattern so as to form four words reading across and five words reading down. No tile may be rotated!

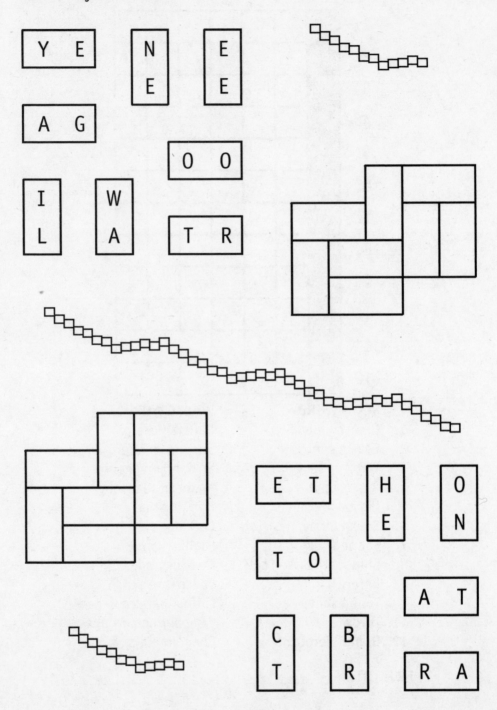

Double Trouble

Solve this one by placing two letters in every square. Each pair of letters reads the same way for both Across and Down words.

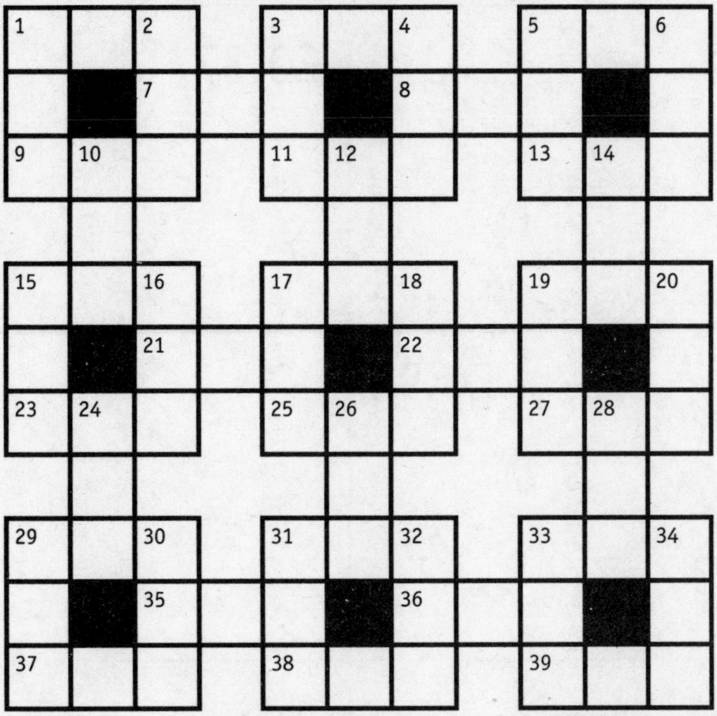

(crossword grid)

Across

1. Scarcity
3. Exchanges
5. Monarch's son
7. Rouse
8. Fate or destiny
9. Certainly, really
11. Electricity generator
13. Top executive
15. Turn white
17. Half asleep
19. Artificial
21. Type of jacket
22. Inactivity
23. Flood of water
25. Respect
27. Specialist
29. Calm, peaceful
31. Shrewdness
33. Dirty
35. Posture, attitude
36. Root vegetable
37. Rail, vilify
38. Remove from office
39. Shout disruptively

Down

1. Keep in custody
2. Melted
3. Fashionable
4. Arctic tribesman
5. Attractive
6. Sri Lanka, formerly
10. Lower in status
12. Slender or limited
14. Stick, cling
15. Fair-haired
16. Transform
17. Male ducks
18. Method
19. For men or women
20. Victoria's husband
24. Brightness or gloss
26. Monotony, dullness
28. Writing implement
29. Strict, harsh
30. Settle comfortably
31. Submit, acquiesce
32. Put a shell around
33. Calm or mitigate
34. Suitable for consumption

Fruit and Veg

Using the totals given, can you calculate the individual prices of each apple, banana, pear and pineapple...

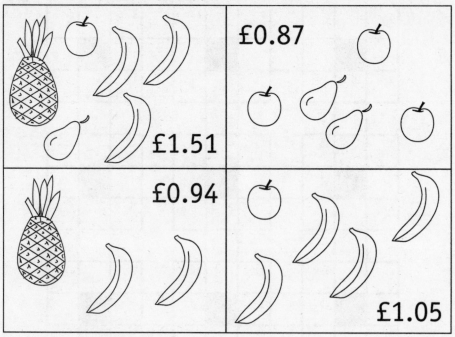

...and each cabbage, carrot, leek and onion?

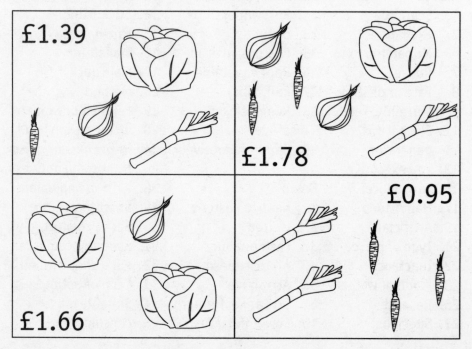

82 *Sidewords*

This puzzle can be solved in one of two ways, starting from either the top left corner or the bottom left corner. Can you find the two sequences of words?

Clues starting Top Left

1. Ensnare (4)

2. A joint in woodwork (5)

3. A hollow between hills (4)

4. A mattress of straw (6)

5. Run competitively (4)

6. A stupid person (4)

7. Obscene or lascivious (4)

Clues starting Bottom Left

1. Lived (5)

2. A vein of ore (4)

3. A business consortium (6)

4. Part of a coat or jacket (5)

5. Turn aside (5)

6. Give or communicate (6)

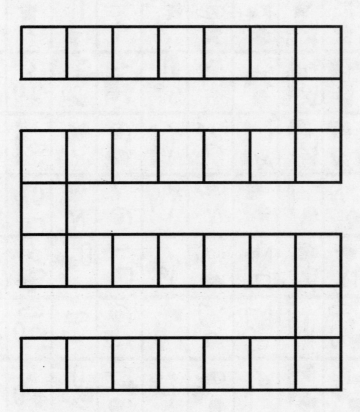

Odd One Out

Each of these rectangles should contain one or more symbols from the numbered rectangle in its particular horizontal row, plus one or more symbols from the lettered rectangle in its particular vertical column. However, one square doesn't follow this rule. Which is the odd one out?

Couplets

The grid below shows a central circle surrounded by shapes, linked to form six sets of three shapes apiece.

Can you place each of the two-letter groups, one per shape, so that every set of three (the central circle, plus the two matching shapes diagonally opposite one another) forms a six-letter word? Whichever pair of letters you place in the central circle will appear in the middle of every word.

OU   OL

ON   CI   ED

TR   EN

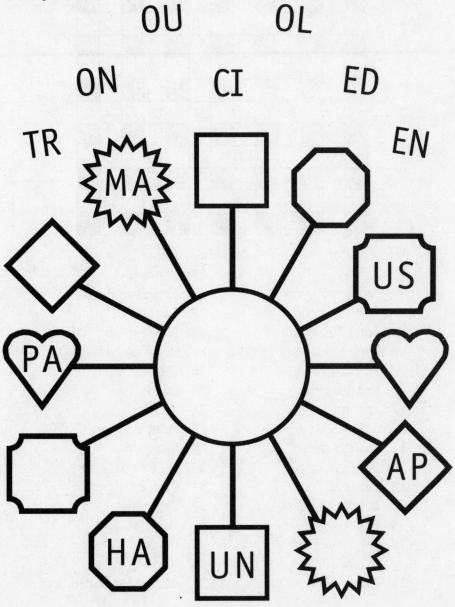

The answer to each clue is a four-letter word, to be entered in the four squares surrounding the corresponding number in the grid. The word can start in any of the four squares and read either clockwise or anticlockwise. The first has already been entered, to get you started.

	Y							
N	1 L	2	3	4	5	6		
	X							
	7	8	9	10	11	12		
	13	14	15	16	17	18		
	19	20	21	22	23	24		
	25	26	27	28	29	30		
	31	32	33	34	35	36		

1. A wildcat
2. Applaud
3. Shaft (of light)
4. Domesticated
5. Smile broadly
6. Competent
7. Way out
8. Not alkaline
9. Remain
10. Joke
11. Twitch, spasm
12. Genuine
13. Engrave
14. Unable to hear
15. Departed
16. Lazy, inactive
17. Slip or slide
18. Flower holder
19. Injure, damage
20. Renown
21. Exploit or deed
22. Slightly wet
23. Poke
24. Urge, persuade
25. Jetty or wharf
26. Cried
27. Verruca
28. Fighting force
29. Red gem
30. Tube or passage
31. Opinion
32. Stake, bet
33. Magic stick
34. Defect
35. A young sheep
36. Percussion instrument

Bermuda Triangle

Travel through the 'Bermuda Triangle' by visiting one room at a time and collecting a letter from each. You can enter the outside passageway as often as you like, but can only visit each room once. When you've completed your tour, rearrange the fifteen letters to spell out a word.

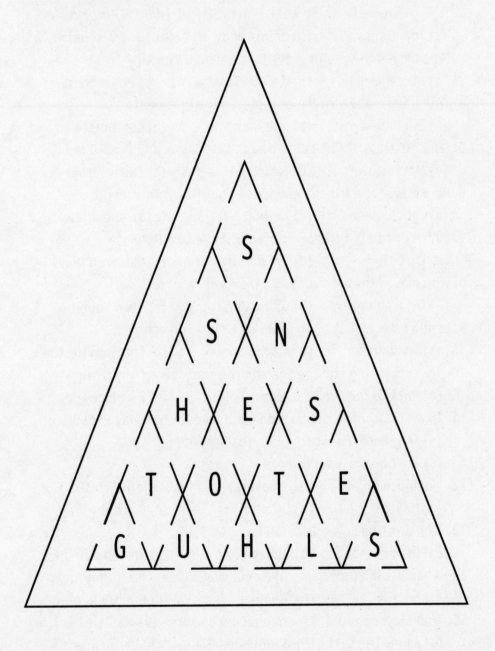

87 The Movie Quiz

Fifteen quiz questions to test your knowledge of the world of movies - you'll be a star if you produce fifteen correct answers, of course!

1. Of what did the murderer have only one in 1993's *The Fugitive*?

   (a) Eye   (b) Ear   (c) Arm

2. Who co-starred with Steve Martin in *Planes, Trains & Automobiles*?

   (a) Tom Hanks   (b) John Candy   (c) Joe Don Baker

3. Who played the villain in the first *Die Hard* movie?

   (a) Alan Rickman   (b) Jeremy Irons   (c) Dennis Franz

4. Which *Independence Day* star played the President?

   (a) Bill Pullman   (b) Will Smith   (c) Jeff Goldblum

5. Which actress has been married to Lee Majors and Ryan O'Neal?

   (a) Mia Farrow   (b) Farrah Fawcett   (c) Carrie Fisher

6. Who played the female lead in the *Look Who's Talking* films?

   (a) Cybill Shepherd   (b) Kathleen Turner   (c) Kirstie Alley

7. Which *Charlie's Angel* co-starred in *A Life Less Ordinary*?

   (a) Lucy Liu   (b) Drew Barrymore   (c) Cameron Diaz

8. Who played the wife in 1993's *Indecent Proposal*?

   (a) Demi Moore   (b) Glenn Close   (c) Sean Young

9. Emilio Estevez is the son of which Hollywood actor?

   (a) Kirk Douglas   (b) Martin Sheen   (c) Charlton Heston

10. *The Quickening* and *The Sorcerer* were sequels to which fantasy?

   (a) *Back To The Future*   (b) *Mad Max*   (c) *Highlander*

11. In which *Star Trek* movie did Ricardo Montalban play the villain?

   (a) *The Search For Spock*   (b) *The Wrath Of Khan*

   (c) *The Undiscovered Country*

12. Mel Gibson played which Shakespearean protagonist in 1990?

   (a) Hamlet   (b) Othello   (c) Macbeth

13. Who directed *Schindler's List*?

   (a) Oliver Stone   (b) Ridley Scott   (c) Steven Spielberg

14. What was the profession of Mel Gibson's character in *Maverick*?

   (a) Sheriff   (b) Gambler   (c) Bounty hunter

15. Who played Arnold Schwarzenegger's wife in 1994's *True Lies*?

   (a) Jamie Lee Curtis (b) Bonnie Bedelia   (c) Sharon Stone

Egg-timer

Can you complete this puzzle in the time it takes to boil an egg?

The answers to the clues are anagrams of the words immediately above and below, plus or minus a letter.

1. To fix securely or deeply
2. Flexible
3. Artists' medium
4. Measure of liquid
5. Sharp end
6. Witch's brew
7. Slice, share

89   *Pyragram*

Solve the anagram on each level of the pyramid and
reveal the hidden word in the central column of bricks.

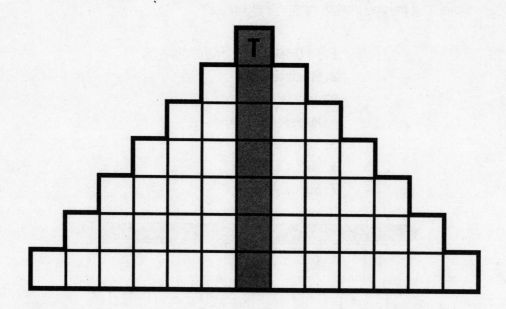

2. Ode

3. Purse

4. My balsa

5. Warm voice

6. Angelic turf

7. Quilt investor

HIDDEN WORD:_____

The clues in this puzzle are all anagrams of their solutions.

DAHAE	KECD / SHARH	▼	DOD / LAISE	▼	RUNAL	▼	GLEAN	▼
L	▼		▼		RUN ►			
CAID ►				MUS		REEL		
⚑			LEAS ►	▼		▼		
SKAR	ALLURE / ROA ►							
⚑		▼	IVE		ODA		ITC	
SOHE	DANOTE		METH	▼	TRA / ARE ►	▼		▼
⚑	▼		▼		▼		TRINE	
DETRAIP		CHOIRE ►					▼	
⚑			YAB		OBA		ETE	
SOHE / MNUB ►			▼	TEB ►	▼		▼	
⚑		ROADE ►						
RHE / YEND ►				ETA ►				

91   *Round the Block*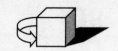

You won't need a starting block to get you under way: because it isn't a race!

Just arrange the 6-letter solutions to the clues into the six blocks around each clue number.

Write the answers in a clockwise direction every time and you'll find that the last answer fits into the first: the main problem will be to decide in which square to put the first letter of each word...

1. Plastic cup
2. Water boiler
3. Covered passageway

4. Rabbits' home
5. Not very wide
6. Twig

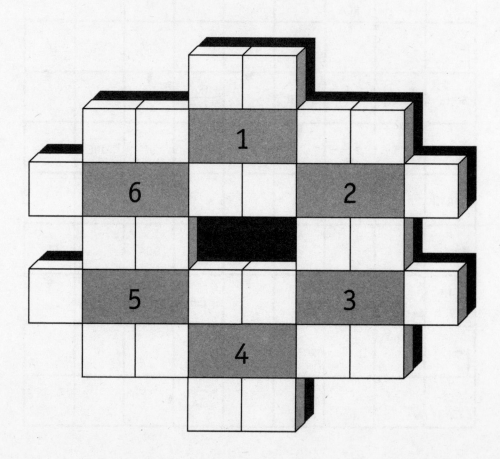

92   *Summing Up*

Arrange one of each of the numbers 2, 3, 6 and 8, as well as one of each of the symbols – (minus), x (times) and + (plus) in every row and column to arrive at the answer at the end of the row or column.

6	x	2	–	8	+	3	=	7
	■		■		■		■	
							=	56
	■		■		■		■	
							=	32
	■		■		■		■	
							=	13
=	■	=	■	=	■	=	■	
26		17		57		28		

93   *Summing Up*

Arrange one of each of the numbers 11, 12, 13 and 14, as well as one of each of the symbols – (minus), x (times) and + (plus) in every row and column to arrive at the answer at the end of the row or column.

11	+	13	x	12	–	14	=	274
	■		■		■		■	
							=	37
	■		■		■		■	
							=	27
	■		■		■		■	
							=	192
=	■	=	■	=	■	=	■	
155		261		339		192		

94 *Figure of Eight*

Solve the clues and enter the answers in the correspondingly numbered squares. The first letter of each word should be entered immediately above the number and the words can read in either a clockwise or anticlockwise direction. A number of letters have already been entered, to start you on your way.

1. The pursuit of pleasure as a matter of ethical principle
2. Critical or constructive response to an inquiry or experiment
3. Strength of character, fortitude
4. Stubbornness or persistent determination
5. Occurring at regular intervals
6. Deserted or abandoned as by an owner
7. Fellow church-members
8. French term for one's 'behind'
9. No longer in use, out of date
10. Cheerfully irresponsible or happy-go-lucky
11. Shattered remains
12. A girl's name or an American state
13. Combustion or start-up
14. Moving, at an emotional level
15. Personal magnetism enabling one to influence others
16. Increase in intensity or extent
17. An official engaged in international negotiations
18. A small, thin, sharp bit or wood or glass or metal
19. Of high moral or intellectual value; elevated in nature or style
20. Obscene, not in keeping with accepted standards of what is right or proper in polite society
21. A brief news report
22. Awkward and clumsy, lacking grace in movement or posture
23. Extend in terms of distance or time

Figure of Eight

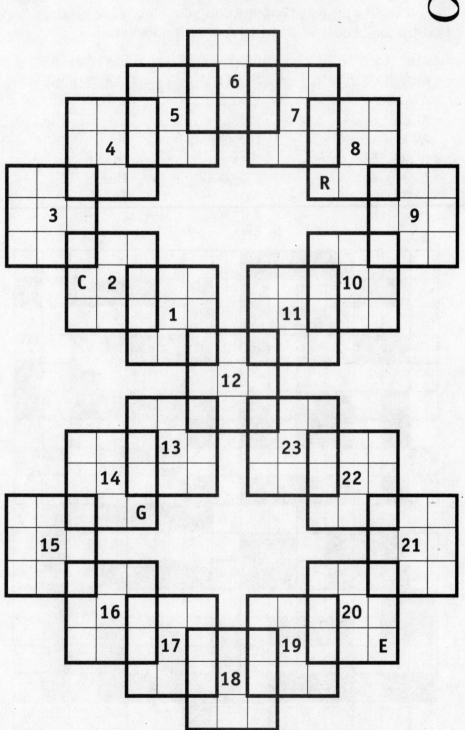

Go with the Flow

Can you fit all of the listed watery words into this grid? Any such as 'Sea of Japan' should be entered as one continuous word.

AIN
ANTARCTIC OCEAN
ARAL SEA
ARNO
AVON
BLACK SEA
CAM
CASPIAN SEA
COMO
EXE

GENEVA
ITCHEN
LAKE ERIE
LOIRE
LOMOND
NILE
ORINOCO
OXUS
PACIFIC
PIT

SEA OF JAPAN
SEA OF OKHOTSK
SEVERN
SOUTH CHINA SEA
SUPERIOR
THAMES
TIGRIS
TWEED
VICTORIA
YELLOW

Downwords

The solutions to the clues are all nine-letter words, the letters for which are contained in the grid below, at the rate of one per line in the correct order. Every letter is used once only.

W	W	T	H	I	I	I	J	K
G	O	R	D	I	A	U	A	M
E	N	A	L	R	R	E	N	S
G	O	T	L	M	L	A	N	G
O	R	P	C	D	A	T	I	I
R	N	N	A	H	O	I	F	W
A	M	C	E	W	I	I	I	O
E	E	R	R	D	O	A	U	C
E	A	R	S	L	D	Y	S	Y

1. Control of one's behaviour

W _ _ _ _ _ _ _ _

2. Across the globe

W _ _ _ _ _ _ _ _

3. Betrayal of a trust

T _ _ _ _ _ _ _ _

4. Mouth organ

H _ _ _ _ _ _ _ _

5. Absolutely alike

I _ _ _ _ _ _ _ _

6. Uneducated person

I _ _ _ _ _ _ _ _

7. Not based on fact, dubious

I _ _ _ _ _ _ _ _

8. Rationalised, shown to be right

J _ _ _ _ _ _ _ _

9. Australian pouched mammals

K _ _ _ _ _ _ _ _

Alphabet Soup

Ladle the letters from the soup tureen and fit one into each of the 26 bowls on the table below, so that the finished result is a complete crossword containing English words. All of the letters in the tureen must be used - thus no letter is used more than once.

	E		R	A			I	S	T	A
E		U		N	E	E		A		
S	A	X	O			E		U	A	
		O			A	R		D		E
Y	U		M				N		P	S
	S		A				E		E	
	E	E		S			O			
E		A		A		E		N		I
R	E	G		L		D	E		E	R
			E	K	E		I		E	
Y	A	R	D	S			E	T	E	

A B C D E F G H I J K
L M N O P Q R S
T U V W X Y Z

98 Whatever Next?

Which circle and its contents should replace the question mark?

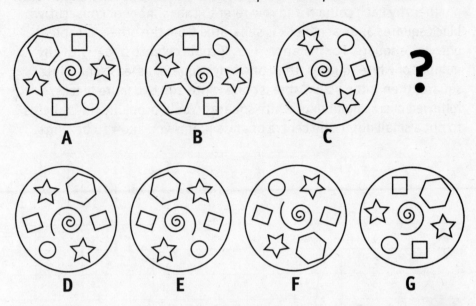

---

99 Hexafit

Can you fit these six words into the hexagons? To fit them all in, some will have to be entered clockwise and others anticlockwise around the numbers. Two letters have been placed already, which should give you a good start!

CHAINS
CHILLY
MIASMA
SLIVER
SMUTTY
VERITY

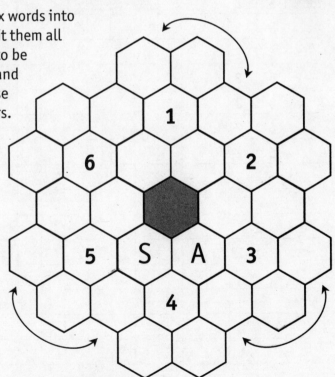

100   *Nonogram*

The grid contains squares that are either black or white. The numbers by each column and row refer to the number of consecutive black squares and each block is separated from the others by at least one white square. For instance, 1, 3, 2 could refer to a row with any number of white squares, then one black square, at least one white square, then three black, at least one white and two more blacks, followed by any number of white squares. You'll probably find it helps to put a small dot in the centre of any squares you know to be white.

	2	1 1	1 1	1 1	5 1 1 1	7 1 1	10 1 1 1	12 1 1	13 1 1 1	13 1 1	1 1 1 1	16 1	2 1 1 1	1 9 1 1	8 1 1 1
2 1															
3 2															
3 3															
4 1															
4 1 1															
5 1 2															
5 1 2															
6 1 2															
6 1 2															
6 1 2															
6 1 2															
6 1 2															
4 4															
2															
2 1															
1 13															
1															
1 1 1 1 1 1															
1															
11															

Many Ways

Starting with the W in the middle of the diamond shaped grid, move either horizontally, vertically or diagonally, from square to square to square, to discover the total number of different ways in which the word WAYS can be spelled out.

			Y			
		Y	A	A		
	S	S	S	S	Y	
Y	A	Y	W	A	S	S
	A	Y	A	Y	S	
		A	Y	S		
			S			

102 Logic Puzzle: Catnip Close

Four families live in Catnip Close; and each owns a cat. Can you match each family with their house number, as well as the name and colour of their cat?

1. The house where Whisky resides has a higher number than the house where the Morton family and their black cat live.

2. Suki lives at No 8, but not with the Mason family.

3. The house where the white cat lives has a higher number than the Monroe residence.

4. Lucky (who doesn't belong to the Mason family) lives in a house with a higher number than that which is home to the ginger cat (who isn't called Toots).

	House No				Cat's name				Colour of cat			
	2	4	6	8	Lucky	Suki	Toots	Whisky	Black	Ginger	Tabby	White
Mason family												
McDonald family												
Monroe family												
Morton family												
Black												
Ginger												
Tabby												
White												
Lucky												
Suki												
Toots												
Whisky												

Family	House No	Cat's name	Colour of cat

103 *Word Ladders*

In this puzzle, you need to change one word into another, by altering one letter at a time. However, the positions of each letter must remain unchanged. Here's an example, changing the word TEA to POT:

T	E	A
P	E	A
P	E	T
P	O	T

Now solve these:

H	I	D	E
S	E	E	K

F	L	E	S	H
B	L	O	O	D

B	R	E	A	D
T	O	A	S	T

104   *All in Place?*

This grid has nine larger squares, each containing room for nine digits. However, not all of the digits are in place.

Replace all of the blanks with the digits 1-9, in such a way that each of the nine larger squares contains nine different digits, as does each row of nine digits reading across and column of nine digits reading downwards.

Every single digit from 1 to 9 appears precisely nine times in total. Below the grid is a check-list which may help - but don't forget to cross off the numbers already in the grid!

2	-	-	-	3	5	-	-	-
-	-	-	2	1	-	5	4	3
-	4	5	-	-	-	-	1	-
9	1	-	-	-	-	-	5	2
4	-	-	-	7	-	-	-	1
5	7	-	-	-	-	-	8	4
-	2	9	-	-	-	-	3	-
-	-	-	7	2	-	9	6	8
7	-	-	-	9	8	-	-	-

1 2 3 4 5 6 7 8 9
1 2 3 4 5 6 7 8 9
1 2 3 4 5 6 7 8 9
1 2 3 4 5 6 7 8 9
1 2 3 4 5 6 7 8 9
1 2 3 4 5 6 7 8 9
1 2 3 4 5 6 7 8 9
1 2 3 4 5 6 7 8 9
1 2 3 4 5 6 7 8 9

105   *Magic Square*

First solve the clues, then write the answers into the grid. The words will read the same across as down.

Situate

Citrus fruit

Correct

African river

To provide

---

106   *Telly-grams*

Can you solve these anagrams, all of which are popular children's TV programmes?

1. PAT COT   _____

2. BAN MAT   _____

3. THIRD BRED SUN   _____

4. FARM IS MEAN   _____

5. TIE BEST BLUE   _____

6. LIFTS ON THE NEST   _____

7. MINI DOG   _____

8. RAG RUTS   _____

9. SEE IT NEW   _____

10. SUE, MO AND REG   _____

Coffee Break

Across

1. Manufacturing plant (7)
5. Venomous snake (5)
8. Very spicy sauce (7)
9. Large North American deer (5)
10. Not now! (5)
11. Versus (7)
12. Type of engine fuel (6)
14. Pay heed (6)
17. Someone who denies the existence of God (7)
19. Not trimmed (5)
22. Be superior to (5)
23. Greek wine (7)
24. Correspond (5)
25. Sea fish (7)

Down

1. Disastrous (5)
2. Explorer who discovered Newfoundland (5)
3. Detect (7)
4. Beefeater (6)
5. Punctuation mark (5)
6. Junior Girl Guide (7)
7. Aroused to a sense of danger (7)
12. Most beloved (7)
13. Moral (7)
15. Baited, teased (7)
16. Stiffening substance used on textiles (6)
18. Filling (5)
20. Egyptian capital (5)
21. Express gratitude (5)

108 *Jigsaw*

Fit the jigsaw together to reveal eight fabrics.

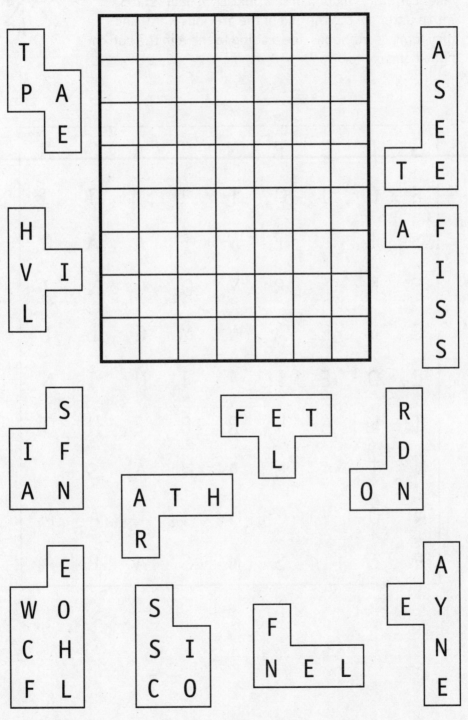

109 *Letter Tracker*

Starting with the G in the top left-hand corner and only moving horizontally or vertically, can you find the eleven American states hidden in this box? Each name starts with a letter next to the end of the previous word, and they form a continuous line leading to the A in the bottom right-hand corner.

G	R	G	R	N	I	A	C	H
E	O	I	O	F	I	M	I	I
S	E	A	E	W	L	A	A	G
S	N	T	R	Y	O	C	N	I
E	N	E	A	W	M	G	L	L
E	D	E	L	A	I	N	I	N
I	M	A	K	R	B	E	N	O
N	T	A	S	A	N	A	S	I
N	O	W	C	O	I	L	A	M
E	S	I	S	N	S	A	B	A

Flow-Words

How many words of three or more different letters can you make from those on the petals, without using plurals, abbreviations or proper nouns?
The central letter must appear in every word.

Letters: R, E, G, N, D, T, A

_____   _____   _____

_____   _____   _____

_____   _____   _____

_____   _____   _____

_____   _____   _____

_____   _____   _____

_____   _____   _____

_____   _____   _____

_____   _____   _____

_____   _____   _____

Each of these vases looks identical at first glance...but they're not!
Every vase differs in one way from the others. Can you spot the
one difference in each case?

112   *Cards on the Table*

What is the face value and suit of each of the cards shown below? Together they total 78. All twelve cards are of different values. In the pack, the values of the cards are as per their numbers and ace = 1, jack = 11, queen = 12 and king = 13. No card is horizontally or vertically next to another of the same colour (hearts and diamonds are red; spades and clubs are black) and there are four different suits in every horizontal row and three different suits in each vertical column.

1. The jack is next to and above the two of hearts, which is next to and right of the seven.
2. The five is next to and left of the ace, which is next to and above the four.
3. The queen (which isn't a spade) is next to and above the eight.
4. Card H has a value two lower than that of card F. Card K has a higher value than that of card E, which is a heart.
5. The nine and ten are not of the same suit; nor are the six and eight.

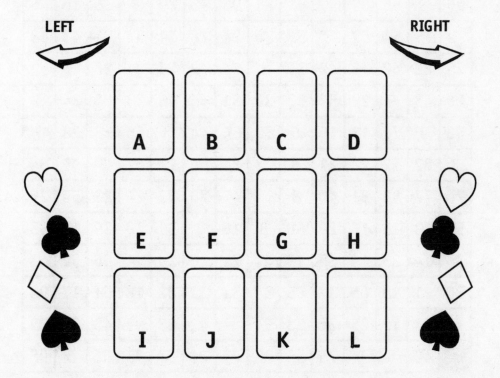

LEFT   RIGHT

113   *Tile Trouble*

Tommy the tiler is in trouble. His terrible niece, Tammy, has set him a problem and he's determined to prove he's good at maths! He has to cross the floor, one tile at a time, starting and ending on the two black tiles, but he can only tread on squares with a number divisible by three and he isn't allowed to move diagonally, nor to jump over any of the tiles. Can you help Tommy get to the bottom of his problem?

START

33	67	81	3	12	3	17	81	8	40	76	31	3	■
8	3	37	31	29	45	58	30	63	48	23	83	21	7
38	18	57	36	78	15	32	90	77	87	89	88	81	3
43	22	11	57	55	12	96	69	41	60	27	45	54	16
65	70	14	90	17	62	88	20	76	63	14	22	27	21
12	3	20	69	36	96	64	82	19	25	76	28	28	63
33	66	61	58	8	87	29	83	73	22	19	34	12	72
99	3	56	63	53	63	51	96	98	29	3	36	16	45
3	75	54	57	3	93	86	27	78	71	33	81	43	13
75	22	42	48	42	39	3	74	72	23	31	25	3	92
26	43	9	22	37	33	32	81	45	43	73	85	34	3
42	3	71	13	19	6	31	54	44	3	66	53	28	9
3	82	12	23	21	9	23	24	66	29	67	3	39	34
76	77	33	31	40	3	55	47	78	33	24	23	54	25
54	18	15	16	29	58	3	16	3	31	72	39	17	33
33	14	23	19	35	13	41	71	76	29	74	66	52	63
30	21	18	65	37	36	34	31	23	22	18	51	17	93
5	17	12	25	36	33	54	87	42	83	99	43	37	23
■	42	6	9	75	55	38	23	21	63	93	61	3	98

114 — *Round Tour*

The answers to this puzzle form a continuous chain, starting at the top left-hand corner and following the direction indicated by the arrows. The last letter of each word is the first letter of the next and each clue is an anagram of its single-word solution. When completed correctly, the shaded squares contain letters which can be rearranged to spell out a mode of transport.

Take care with this one, as sometimes it is possible to form more than one word from the letters in the clue.

1. Sticks to

2. Idolater

3. Tubed

4. Hectare

5. Eric

6. Live

7. Clean

8. Aeries

9. Tapers

10. Latent

11. Dry net

12. Gory hut

13. Tort

Start

Transport: _____

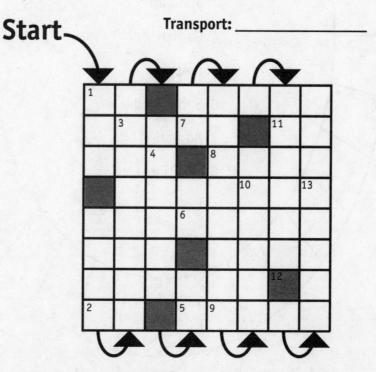

115 Roundword

Write the answer to each clue in a clockwise direction. Every solution overlaps the next by either one, two or three letters and each solution starts in its numbered section. The solution to the final clue ends with the letter in the first square.

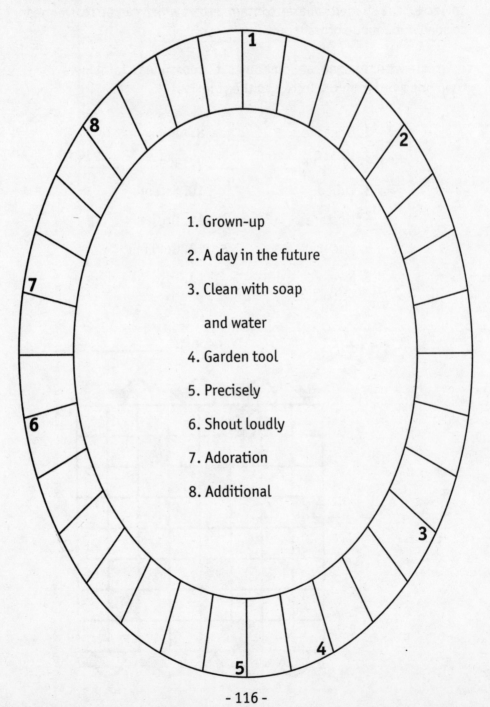

1. Grown-up

2. A day in the future

3. Clean with soap and water

4. Garden tool

5. Precisely

6. Shout loudly

7. Adoration

8. Additional

The vowels A, E, I, O and U have been removed from the crossword below. Can you replace them correctly? When you have, the first and last letters of every complete word containing an O can be rearranged to form another word.

S	P		T		L				
Y		L		N				R	N
C		L	M		S		T		Q
							H		
P			R		S		C		P
H			G				R		
				B		R			N
N				S		S			L
T			S		T			T	Y

A A A A A A A

E E E E E E E E E

I I I I I

O O

U U U U

HIDDEN WORD: _____

A Cut Above

This crossword has been cut into many pieces. Can you reassemble it? We've placed some, to give you a start.

118 *The Geography Quiz*

A dozen quiz questions to test your knowledge of the world - you'll feel on top of the world if you pick twelve correct answers, of course!

1. The Hoover Dam is situated on which lake?

    (a) Mead   (b) Superior   (c) Tahoe   (d) Huron

2. Which Strait separates Alaska from Russia?

    (a) Bass   (b) Sunda   (c) Davis   (d) Bering

3. In which Australian state is Ayers Rock?

    (a) Western Australia   (b) ACT   (c) Northern Territory

    (d) Queensland

4. In which region is Ben Nevis?

    (a) Pennines   (b) Trossachs   (c) Snowdon

    (d) Grampians

5. The Galapagos Islands are part of which country?

    (a) Chile   (b) Paraguay   (c) Ecuador   (d) Argentina

6. What is the Hindu Kush?

    (a) River   (b) Mountain range   (c) Lake   (d) Volcano

7. In which part of Africa is Mauritania?

    (a) W Africa   (b) E Africa   (c) N Africa   (d) S Africa

8. Where is Phnom Penh?

    (a) Cambodia   (b) Laos   (c) Myanmar   (d) Vietnam

9. Vilnius is the capital of which country?

    (a) Latvia   (b) Estonia   (c) Belarus   (d) Lithuania

10. Where is the Guadalquivir river?

    (a) Bolivia   (b) Portugal   (c) Spain   (d) Brazil

11. The Suez Canal connects the Gulf of Suez with which sea?

    (a) Mediterranean   (b) Arabian   (c) Aral   (d) Coral

12. What is the capital of Pakistan?

    (a) Karachi   (b) Islamabad   (c) Dacca   (d) Lahore

119 *Breakfast Treat*

Here's one to get your teeth into! Eggs-actly what you need to start your day... Why not save this one for breakfast-time?

Across

4. Hoot with derision (3)
6. Torture (5)
9. Example (8)
10. Own (7)
14. Outbuilding for housing a car (6)
15. Mischievous imp (7)
16. Necessity (4)
17. Precipitating as a mixture of rain and snow (8)
20. Very large stone forming part of a prehistoric structure (8)
22. Literary composition (5)
25. Self-justification (5)
27. Use inefficiently (5)
30. President (8)
31. Lineage (8)
34. Kitty (4)
35. Canal (7)
36. Frustrate (6)
37. Oxygenated (7)
39. Deprived of parents by death or desertion (8)
40. Endure (5)
41. Ovum (3)

Down

1. Bottomless gulf or pit (5)
2. Lessen the intensity of (8)
3. District (4)
5. Paper-folding art (7)
7. Retaliation (7)
8. Forgiving under provocation (8)
11. Showy, flowering garden plant (6)
12. Parasol (8)
13. Conjecture (5)
18. Expel from one's property (5)
19. Three-wheeled bike (8)
21. Long period of time (3)
23. More alien (8)
24. — Khan (3)
26. Crescent-shaped yellow fruit (6)
28. Condiment (5)
29. Oriental (7)
32. Byre (7)
33. Shrivelled, wizened (8)
37. Old saying or proverb (5)
38. Sudden attack (4)

Breakfast Treat

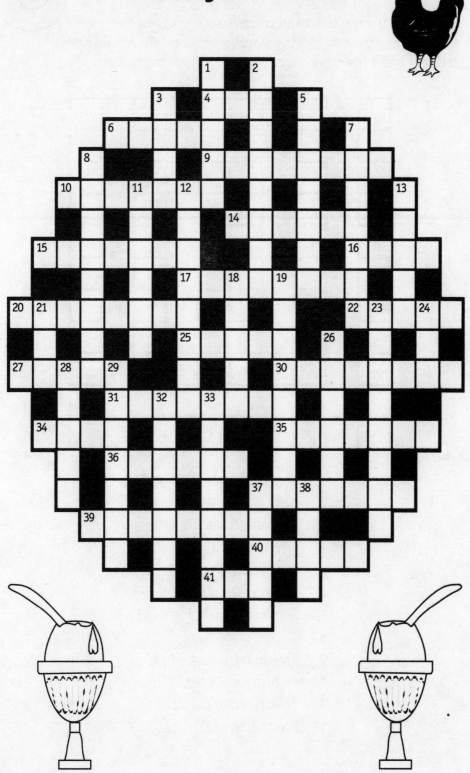

120   *In-Words*

Starting at the top left-hand corner, work your way to
the centre of the grid. All the words overlap by either one or two
letters - and a few have already been entered, to start you off...

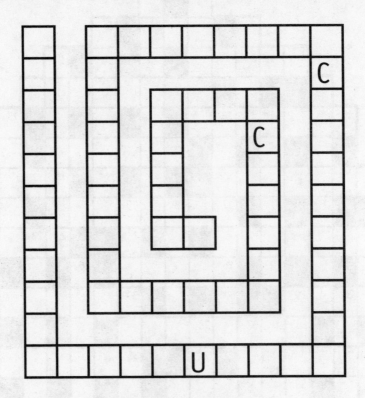

1.   Aggressive, unfriendly (7)
2.   Make or pass laws (9)
3.   Alcoholic drink from Mexico (7)
4.   Hired killer (8)
5.   Harmless (9)
6.   Theatre attendant (5)
7.   Burst or explode forth (5)
8.   Violent storm (7)
9.   Ascendancy, control (9)
10.   An historical age (5)
11.   Of little value (5)
12.   Dress, attire (7)

121 Around the Squares

The answer to each clue is a four-letter word, to be entered in the four squares surrounding the corresponding number in the grid. The word can start in any of the four squares and read either clockwise or anticlockwise. The first has already been entered, to get you started.

	R							
E	1	0	2	3	4	5	6	
	S							
	7	8	9	10	11	12		
	13	14	15	16	17	18		
	19	20	21	22	23	24		
	25	26	27	28	29	30		
	31	32	33	34	35	36		

1. Garden flower
2. Not closed
3. Walk through water
4. Opera star
5. Metal, symbol Fe
6. Rounded shape
7. Bridge
8. Severe ache
9. Moist
10. Fall
11. Close to
12. Adore
13. Fire from job
14. Religious picture
15. Grumble
16. Item of footwear
17. Capable
18. Otherwise
19. Monarch
20. African beast
21. Lend
22. Halt
23. Go by boat
24. Told fibs
25. Part of a bird
26. Lengthy
27. Mislay
28. Cheeky
29. Chum
30. Post
31. Double
32. Bird's home
33. Rescue
34. Fit of anger
35. Orange rind
36. Treaty, agreement

122 *Sidewords*

This puzzle can be solved in one of two ways, starting from either the top left corner or the bottom left corner. Can you find the two sequences of words?

Clues starting Top Left

1. Rind (4)

2. Italian sausage (6)

3. To do with birth (5)

4. Obsessive fixation (6)

5. Strong rope or flex (5)

6. Ingrained dirt (5)

Clues starting Bottom Left

1. An Arab chieftain (4)

2. Colloidal jelly (3)

3. German composer (4)

4. A piece of land (4)

5. Smooth (4)

6. Living creature (6)

7. Unconscious (6)

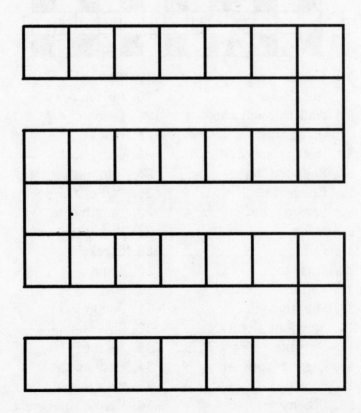

123   *Where the L?*

Twelve L-shapes like the ones below have been inserted
in the grid. Each L has one hole in it. There are three pieces
of each of the four kinds shown below and any piece might be turned
or flipped over before being put in the grid. No two pieces of the
same kind touch, even at a corner. The pieces fit together so well
that you cannot see the spaces between them, only the holes show.
Can you tell where the Ls are?

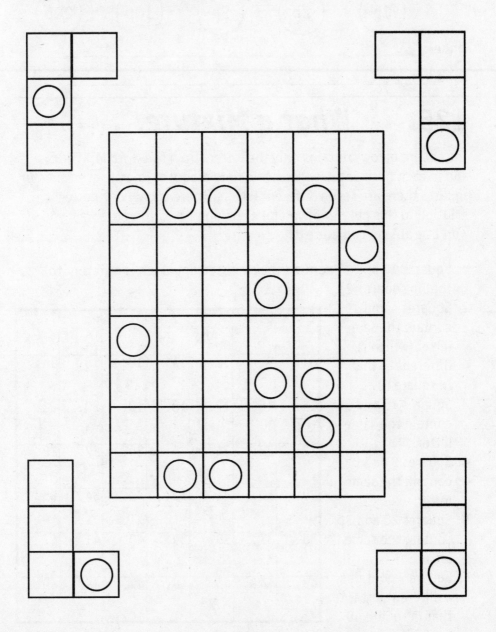

124   Loose Change

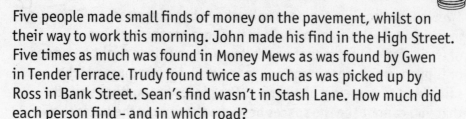

Five people made small finds of money on the pavement, whilst on their way to work this morning. John made his find in the High Street. Five times as much was found in Money Mews as was found by Gwen in Tender Terrace. Trudy found twice as much as was picked up by Ross in Bank Street. Sean's find wasn't in Stash Lane. How much did each person find - and in which road?

| 1p | 2p | 5p | 10p | 20p |

Finder: _____ _____ _____ _____ _____

Road: _____ _____ _____ _____ _____

---

125   What a Mixture!

The square below contains only the letters from the word MIXTURE and in each horizontal, vertical and long diagonal line of seven smaller squares there are seven different letters. There is only one correct solution to this puzzle - if you take a wrong path along the way, you won't be able to complete it!

1. Squares 11 and 17 contain the same letter (which is different to that in square 42).
2. Squares 4 and 19 contain the same letter (which is different to that in square 8).
3. Squares 13 and 38 contain the same letter.
4. Squares 5 and 9 contain the same letter.
5. Squares 20 and 36 contain the same letter.
6. Square 7 contains a different letter to that in square 40.

1.	2.	3. M	4.	5.	6.	7.
8.	9.	10.	11.	12. U	13.	14.
15. I	16.	17.	18.	19.	20.	21. E
22.	23.	24.	25.	26.	27. R	28.
29.	30.	31. T	32.	33.	34.	35.
36.	37.	38.	39.	40.	41.	42.
43.	44.	45. X	46.	47.	48.	49.

126 *Trees Company*

Can you fit all of these tree-related words into the grid?

ASH
BAY
ELM
MAY
NUT
OAK
YEW

ABELE
APPLE
ASPEN
LARCH
LEMON

BANANA
BRANCH
RUBBER

ACER
BARK
BEAM
CONE
CORK
PLUM
TEAK

MAGNOLIA

Each of the thirty-six squares in the grid is filled with a single digit number from 1 to 9 - each of those numbers being used four times. Use the clues to complete the square, bearing in mind that the same number must not appear in two adjacent (touching) squares either across or down. If the same number is used more than once in any row across or column down, it is stated in the relevant clue.

Across:
1. Total twenty-one.
2. Total thirty-nine.
3. Consecutive numbers placed in order.
4. The highest and lowest digits are adjacent.
5. Two nines.
6. Total twenty-one.

Down:
1. Two nines. Two is the lowest digit.
2. Consecutive numbers placed in order.
3. Two threes. Total twenty-one.
4. Two eights. No four.
5. Two sixes. Total forty.
6. No seven.

	1	2	3	4	5	6
1						
2						
3						
4						
5						
6						

128

ARROWWORD

Grid clues:

- Thrifty
- Guardian
- Repent
- Newts
- Section of play
- Domestic ass
- Broker
- Frequently
- Transported
- Muslim prayer-leader
- Glide on snow
- Put on golf peg
- Whole
- Repute
- Part of collar
- Form of address
- Pop singer
- Stamp
- Spotted
- Valuable quality
- Less deep
- Ripped
- Heavenly body
- Port in NW Italy
- Greek goddess
- Chum
- Sprocket
- Legend
- Mineral
- Spanish cry of support
- Malleable
- Wrath
- Portent
- Hard fruits
- Globe
- Lived
- Sicilian volcano
- Jog
- Type of cloth
- Bed-linen items
- Noah's boat
- Puts up
- Australian bear
- Boy's name
- Burned remains
- Mend
- Cereal
- Listening organ
- Penultimate Greek letter
- Mr Reed (*Perfect Day*)
- Heap
- Beer
- Divisive
- Native of eg Glasgow

129 Round the Block

You won't need a starting block to get you under way: because it isn't a race!

Just arrange the 6-letter solutions to the clues into the six blocks around each clue number.

Write the answers in a clockwise direction every time and you'll find that the last answer fits into the first: the main problem will be to decide in which square to put the first letter of each word...

1. Sturdy, durable
2. Heavily carved or jewelled
3. Type of fuel

4. Heavenly body
5. Thawed
6. Twice the quantity

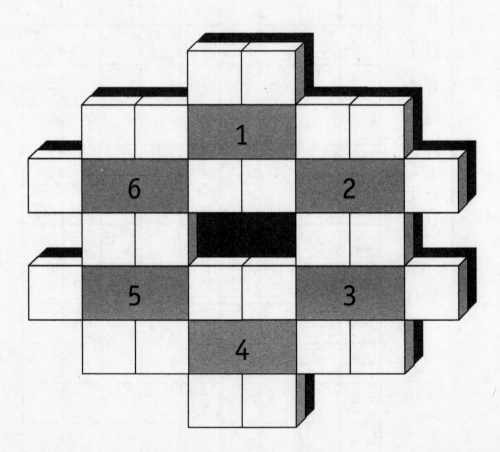

Coffee Break

Across

1. Unwrinkled (6)
4. Duty (6)
8. Implied (5)
10. Black and white, bamboo-eating mammal (5)
11. Deciduous conifer (5)
12. Hire (5)
14. Concur (5)
16. Equality (3)
18. Wheel shaft (4)
19. First man (4)
21. Alcoholic spirit (3)
24. Swim (5)
27. Plasma (5)
29. Embellish (5)
30. Keen (5)
31. Wrath (5)
32. Peevish (6)
33. Type of insect (6)

Down

1. Plain (6)
2. Largest city in Nebraska (5)
3. Identifying appellation (5)
5. First letter of the Greek alphabet (5)
6. Interior (5)
7. Worn away or tattered (6)
9. Expanse (4)
13. Half of one third (5)
15. Serious (5)
16. Wooden pin (3)
17. Went faster (3)
20. Item (6)
22. Metallic element, symbol Fe (4)
23. Come forth (6)
25. Constricted (5)
26. Soil (5)
27. Serpent (5)
28. Correct (5)

131 *Skeleton*

Given just three clue numbers and three black squares, can you solve this crossword? When the puzzle is complete, the pattern of the black squares will be symmetrical.

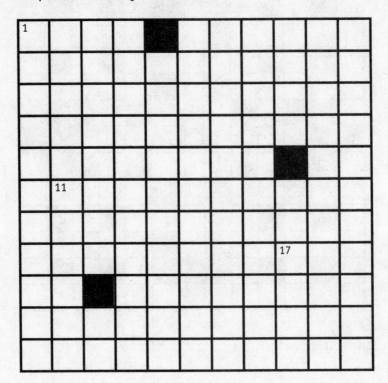

Across

1. Conspire
6. Murmur discontentedly
7. Sanctuary
9. Joy or satisfaction
10. An item in a list
12. Confidence
15. Artificial
16. Intelligent
18. Fatness
19. Warmth

Down

1. Gratify
2. Carry out
3. Theatrical entertainment
4. Leave the country
5. Paying customer
8. Generosity
11. In the vicinity
13. Solitary man
14. Sharp
17. Foul or loathsome

132   *The Bottom Line*

The bottom line of this grid is waiting to be filled.

Every square in the solution contains only one shape from rows 1-4 above, although two or more squares in the solution may contain the same shape. At the end of every numbered row is a score, which shows:

a. the number of shapes placed in the correct finishing position on the bottom line, as indicated by a tick;

and

b. the number of shapes which appear on the bottom line, but in a different position, as indicated by a cross.

Can you fill each of the four squares with the correct shape?

					Score
1	♥	○	☐	♣	✓
2	△	♠	◆	☆	X X X
3	☐	△	☆	◆	X X
4	☆	♥	○	△	✓
					✓✓✓✓

Codeword

Each number in the grid represents a different letter of the alphabet. You need to decipher the code and fill in the crossword. A checking grid is provided, which may be of help - and we've filled in three of the letters, to get you off to a good start...but beware: one letter will remain unused and its value is the only unallocated number, so this Codeword isn't quite as easy as those earlier in the book.

A B C D E F G H I J K L M

N O P Q R S T U V W X Y Z

7		3		24		12		14		9		2		18
25	16	26	21	26	21	26		26	9	25	2	3	21	6
19		2		15		4		10		2		20		13
19	15	19	19	21	26	20		14	18	20	23	25	19	18
21		21				26		15		20		13		26
26	21	26	1	26	8	14	2	21		26	2	14	26	8
			1					26		21		21		26
2	4	20	23	3	2	14		12	13	21	2	6	26	5
20		26		20		26				26				
2	25	5	15	23		2	9	25	26	5	25	4	14	12
3		26		15		3		13				23		26
15	8	12	15	5	26	20		22	15	17	26	8	26	5
2		15		26		26		2		26		24		2
8	15	19	26	20	15	2		20	26	12	13	26	4	14
12		8		6		16		5		14		10		26

1	2	3	4	5 D	6	7	8	9 Q	10	11	12	13
14	15	16	17	18	19	20 R	21	22	23	24	25	26

134 *Dice-Section*

Printed onto every one of the six numbered dice
seen stacked below are six letters (one per side), which
can be rearranged to form the answer to the clue for each die.
The problem is, you can only see three sides of any die! Use the
clues to solve the six-letter answers, writing them into the grid.
When correctly filled, the highlighted letters in the grid, read in
the order 1-6, will spell out another word, meaning: look.

1. Boundary, border
2. Purse
3. Mend
4. Capital city
5. Zodiacal sign
6. Turn to ice

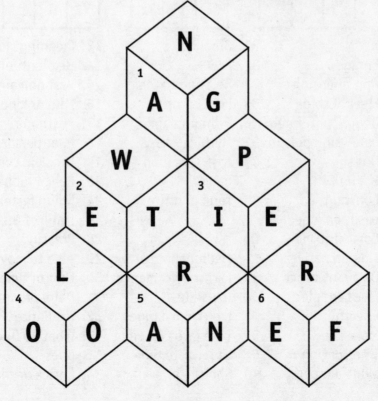

135 Double Trouble !!

Solve this one by placing two letters in every square. Each pair of letters reads the same way for both Across and Down words.

Across
1. Enrage
3. Apprehension
5. Fleet of ships
7. Rough, unrefined
8. Paralysing poison
9. On land
11. Put up with
13. Constant, not easily changed
15. Come into view
17. Tibetan native
19. Delay, obstruct
21. Five cent piece
22. Cheerful
23. Make known
25. Thin coating
27. Moneylender
29. Gloomy
31. Fee
33. Relating to teeth
35. Popular drink
36. Swift and agile
37. Mythical story
38. Irish Christian name
39. Term of office

Down
1. Medium hot curry
2. Extra performance
3. Invisible
4. Free from danger
5. Take into custody
6. Lag, waste time
10. Shout
12. Cleaning cloth
14. Be plentiful
15. Vast domain
16. Mild or kindly
17. Postpone
18. Poor person
19. Break in continuity
20. Pencil rubber
24. Nylon fastener
26. Drink of the gods
28. Pressing
29. Able to move
30. Unit of time
31. Dairy product
32. Brilliance
33. What 20 Down does
34. Entice or charm

136   *Simple as A, B, C?*   ABC

Each of the small squares in the grid below contains either A, B or C.
Every row, column and each of the two long diagonals has exactly
two of each letter. The information in the clues refers only to the
squares in that row or column. To help you solve this problem, we
have given as many clues as we think you will need! Can you tell the
letter in each square?

Across:

1. The Cs are between the Bs.

2. The Bs are further right than the Cs.

5. The Bs are further right than the As.

6. The Bs are further right than the As.

Down:

4. The Bs are higher than the Cs.

5. The Bs are lower than the Cs.

6. The Cs are between the Bs.

	1	2	3	4	5	6
1						
2						
3						
4						
5						
6						

137 Logic Puzzle: Snakes Alive!

The 80's punk group 'Snakes Alive' disbanded many years ago but some of their memorabilia has recently come up for auction, including a signed poster. The poster shows the real name of each band member along with his stage name. Can you work out each man's stage name, together with his position in the group?

1. Ray's stage name was Viper; and the bass player's was Cobra.
2. Dave wasn't the keyboard player.
3. The drummer's stage name began with the same letter as his real name.
4. Chris was either the lead singer or the man nicknamed Boa.
5. The lead guitarist has a real name which is longer than the real name of the man whose stage name was Python.

	Stage Name					Position in Group				
	Boa	Cobra	Python	Rattler	Viper	Bass guitar	Drums	Keyboard	Lead guitar	Lead singer
Chris										
Colin										
Dave										
Ray										
Rick										
Bass guitar										
Drums										
Keyboard										
Lead guitar										
Lead singer										

Band member	Stage name	Position in group

138   Domino Placement

A standard set of 28 dominoes has been laid out as shown. Can you draw in the edges of them all? The check-box is provided as an aid and one domino has already been placed.

5	1	6	5	4	0	3
3	0	2	3	4	5	4
2	6	2	3	1	6	3
4	4	5	1	6	1	6
5	0	4	2	6	1	0
2	3	5	0	0	3	2
6	4	5	4	1	2	1
0	5	3	1	6	0	2

0-0	0-1	0-2	0-3	0-4	0-5	0-6

1-1	1-2	1-3	1-4	1-5	1-6	2-2

2-3	2-4	2-5	2-6	3-3	3-4	3-5

3-6	4-4	4-5	4-6	5-5	5-6	6-6

Fill-In

Using the list of words below, can you fill in this crossword?
Every word is used once only and all are required to fill the grid.

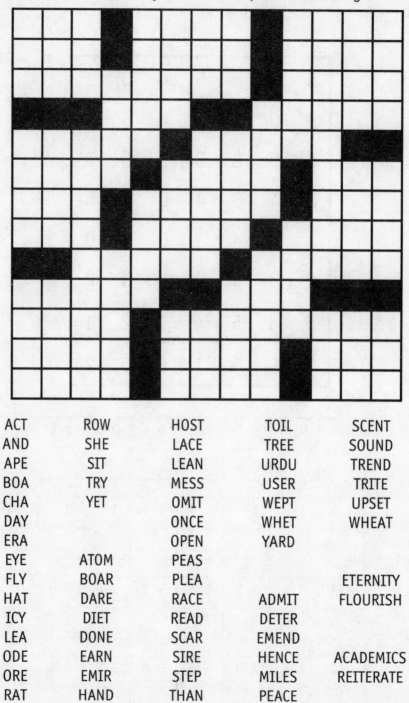

ACT	ROW	HOST	TOIL	SCENT
AND	SHE	LACE	TREE	SOUND
APE	SIT	LEAN	URDU	TREND
BOA	TRY	MESS	USER	TRITE
CHA	YET	OMIT	WEPT	UPSET
DAY		ONCE	WHET	WHEAT
ERA		OPEN	YARD	
EYE	ATOM	PEAS		
FLY	BOAR	PLEA		ETERNITY
HAT	DARE	RACE	ADMIT	FLOURISH
ICY	DIET	READ	DETER	
LEA	DONE	SCAR	EMEND	
ODE	EARN	SIRE	HENCE	ACADEMICS
ORE	EMIR	STEP	MILES	REITERATE
RAT	HAND	THAN	PEACE	

140   *Flow-Words*

How many words of three or more different letters can
you make from those on the petals, without using plurals,
abbreviations or proper nouns?
The central letter must appear in every word.

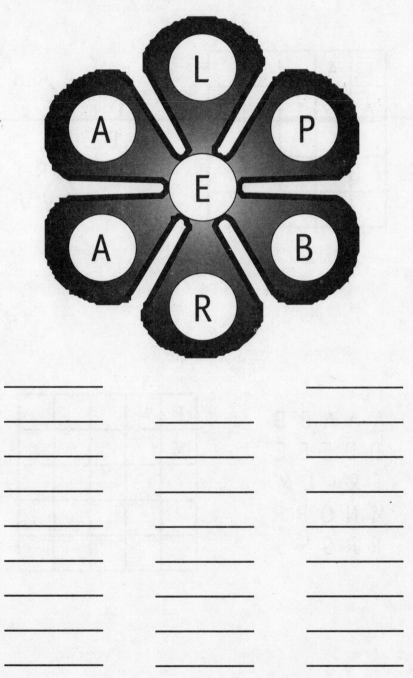

_____   _____   _____

_____   _____   _____

_____   _____   _____

_____   _____   _____

_____   _____   _____

_____   _____   _____

_____   _____   _____

141   *Magic Squares*

Use every letter to the side of each grid to fill the crossword completely, in such a way that each crossword reads the same across as down. For each crossword, three letters have been given as a start.

L	A			
A				

A ~~A~~ A ~~A~~ B
D E E E
E E ~~E~~ L L
O O R R T
T T T V V

A A A B B
D D E E E
E ~~E~~ L L ~~M~~
~~M~~ N O R R
R R S S S

E	M			
M				

Pyragram

Solve the anagram on each level of the pyramid and reveal the hidden word in the central column of bricks.

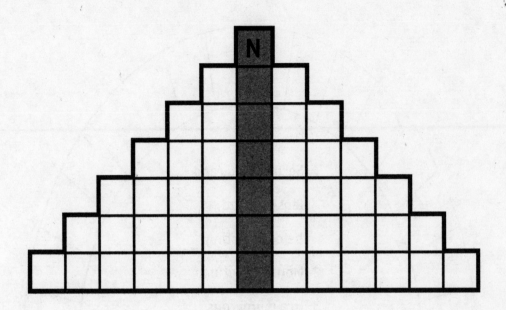

2. Who

3. Manor

4. Cold tea

5. Hold boots

6. Similar meat

7. Run on optician

HIDDEN WORD:_____

143 *Roundword*

Write the answer to each clue in a clockwise direction.
Every solution overlaps the next by either one, two or three letters
and each solution starts in its numbered section. The solution to the
final clue ends with the letter in the first square.

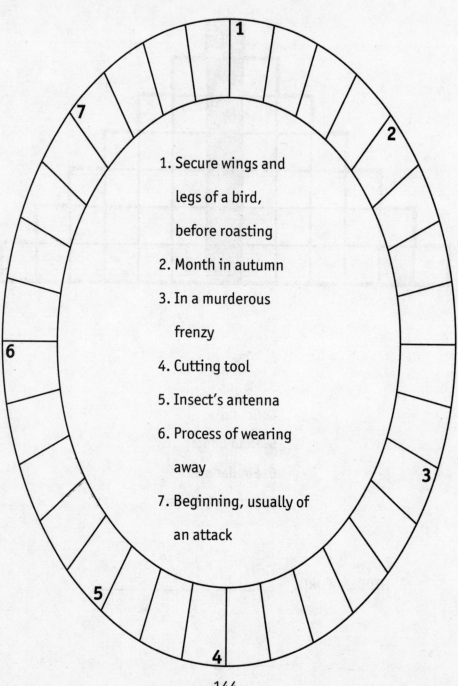

1. Secure wings and

   legs of a bird,

   before roasting

2. Month in autumn

3. In a murderous

   frenzy

4. Cutting tool

5. Insect's antenna

6. Process of wearing

   away

7. Beginning, usually of

   an attack

144   *Spiral Crossword*

Fill in the answers to each clue in a spiralling direction.
The last letter of one word becomes the first letter of the next.

1. In place of
2. Child
3. Re-establishment of good relations
4. Attribute of mischievous children
5. Horse trained to race over hurdles
6. Understanding, recognising
7. Relating to cuisine
8. In a rigidly formal manner
9. Longing for
10. Pregnancy
11. No matter what
12. Performing acrobatic feats
13. Cultivator of land near house
14. Reinstatement
15. Myopic
16. The spreading of power away from government
17. Not on either side
18. English county
19. Became knowledgeable through participation
20. Feeling distaste for
21. Idle chatter
22. A leisurely walk in a public place
23. Seismic tremor

Extensowords

w-o-r-d-s

The beginning of each word in this grid is a word in itself, separately clued. When the puzzle is completed, the letters in the shaded vertical column will reveal a well-known motto.

1.
2.
3.
4.
5.
6.
7.
8.
9.
10.
11.
12.

	START WORD	WHOLE WORD
1.	A dam across a river	In a strange way
2.	Sharpen	Truthfulness
3.	Egg cells	Enthusiastic reception
4.	A hollow in a surface	'Tooth' doctor
5.	Trouble or difficulty	Taken in
6.	Flushed	Compensation
7.	Greek love-god	Gradual decay
8.	A mineral spring	Simple and austere
9.	The side of a building	Small marsupial
10.	Anger	European country
11.	Devoid of feeling	Old Testament book
12.	Con trick	Skitter

MOTTO: _____

Each of the thirty-six squares in the grid is filled with a single digit number from 1 to 9 - each of those numbers being used four times. Use the clues to complete the square, bearing in mind that the same number must not appear in two adjacent (touching) squares either across or down. If the same number is used more than once in any row across or column down, it is stated in the relevant clue.

Across:
1. Two nines. No even numbers.
2. Total thirty-eight.
3. Total twenty-one.
4. Two sixes.
5. The highest and lowest digits are adjacent. Total twenty-two.
6. Two eights. No seven.

Down:
1. Two twos. Two sevens. No one.
2. Two eights.
3. Two nines. Total forty-four.
4. Consecutive numbers placed in order.
5. Two threes. No two.
6. Two ones. No nine. Total nineteen.

	1	2	3	4	5	6
1						
2						
3						
4						
5						
6						

147 Jigsaw

Fit the jigsaw together to reveal eight alcoholic drinks.

148   Round the Block

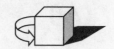

You won't need a starting block to get you under way:
because it isn't a race!

Just arrange the 6-letter solutions to the clues into the six blocks
around each clue number.

Write the answers in a clockwise direction every time and you'll find
that the last answer fits into the first: the main problem will be to
decide in which square to put the first letter of each word...

1. Part of the week
2. Not so thin!
3. Cups and saucers, etc (3-3)
4. Salty
5. Taken to, by car
6. Share out

Cryptic Crossword

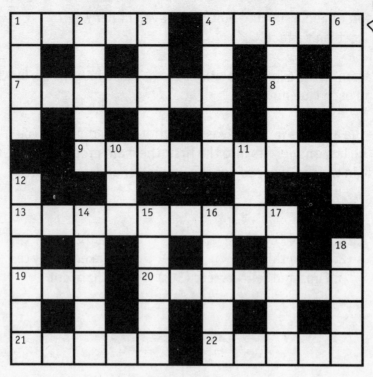

Across

1. Put up with a follower beside castle (5)
4. Hammer donated by leading lady (5)
7. Cop-out arranged by small ocean-dweller (7)
8. Cut record without love (3)
9. Conserve drink for a reason (9)
13. Seasoning not minced badly (9)
19. Ruin contrary sheep (3)
20. Confidential talk about four (7)
21. Thought student perfect (5)
22. Fashion shirt with split (5)

Down

1. Kick first-timer after a critical sound (4)
2. Notepad unopened for mammal (5)
3. Placed beyond spirit and broken (5)
4. Relish blast on second horn (5)
5. Not well inside Virginia's house (5)
6. Fallen quarters held by US cops (6)
10. Assist one in commercial setting (3)
11. Not one outspoken holy woman (3)
12. Seafood swindle by investigator (6)
14. Tend translated runes (5)
15. Force scallywag ahead of the Spanish (5)
16. Order cited incorrectly (5)
17. Swap twisted missile with Asian (5)
18. Exploit flower with deformed top (4)

150 *Summing Up*

Arrange one of each of the numbers 3, 5, 7 and 9, as well as one of each of the symbols – (minus), x (times) and + (plus) in every row and column to arrive at the answer at the end of the row or column.

7	–	5	x	3	+	9	=	15
							=	29
							=	49
							=	41
=		=		=		=		
26		17		57		28		

151 *Summing Up*

Arrange one of each of the numbers 2, 4, 6 and 7, as well as one of each of the symbols – (minus), x (times) and + (plus) in every row and column to arrive at the answer at the end of the row or column.

7	+	2	–	4	x	6	=	30
							=	19
							=	9
							=	22
=		=		=		=		
24		28		32		44		

152 *The Big One*

Have fun with this GIANT crossword - straightforward clues requiring straightforward answers...well, mostly...!

Across

1. An open-air meal (6)
4. Pause uncertainly (6)
8. Germany as an empire (5)
9. Called off, abandoned (7)
10. Beneath (5)
11. A drinking cup or bowl (7)
12. Unwell (3)
13. Expel from a dwelling (5)
14. Liquorice-flavoured oil (7)
15. A proposition to be proved (7)
17. Relating to the nose (5)
20. In bad condition (5)
21. An inhabitant or citizen (7)
22. A layer of rock (7)
24. Ignite (5)
25. Goliath's opponent (5)
28. Badly behaved (7)
31. A chain of related leaders (7)
32. Of meat, dried and salted (5)
34. Deliberately deceive (3)
35. Walk unsteadily (7)
36. A bird's perch or bed (5)
37. Mammals or brutes (7)
38. Not of this world (5)
39. Put right (6)
40. Anger, infuriate (6)

Down

1. Lie under oath (7)
2. Naively innocent (9)
3. The beneficiary of a will (9)
5. Intense love (9)
6. Poor and shabby condition (9)
7. Someone with scarlet hair? (7)
9. Highly praised (9)
15. Bundled or tied up (7)
16. The Japanese art of paper-folding (7)
18. Putting up with (7)
19. Long in duration (7)
23. Entirely without cash (9)
26. Wanton destruction (9)
27. The instrument panel of a car (9)
29. Subject to doubt (9)
30. A mouth-organ (9)
31. Lack of hope (7)
33. The easing of strained relations (7)

153 *Sidewords*

This puzzle can be solved in one of two ways, starting from either the top left corner or the bottom left corner. Can you find the two sequences of words?

Clues starting Top Left

1. Exchange (5)

2. Have import (6)

3. Touched (4)

4. Gentle or delicate (6)

5. A Greek letter (4)

6. A dance form (6)

Clues starting Bottom Left

1. Inform (4)

2. Lessen, subside (5)

3. Reproduced (4)

4. Sting or annoy (6)

5. Worry (4)

6. Domesticated (5)

7. A practical skill (3)

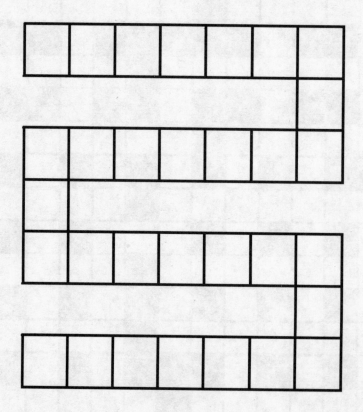

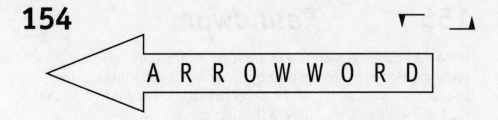

ARROWWORD

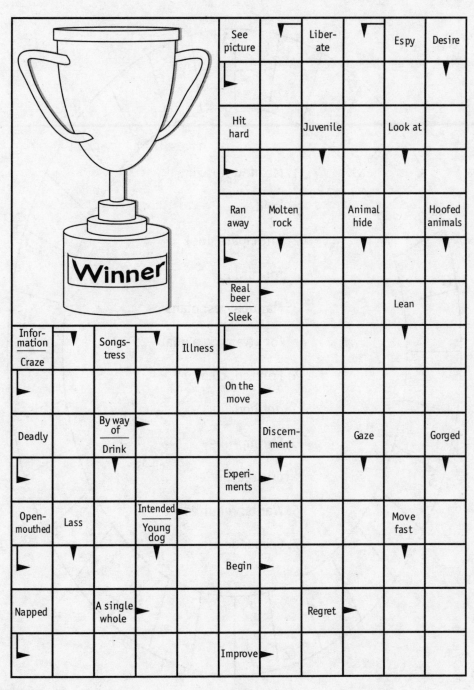

See picture	▼	Liber-ate	▼	Espy	Desire
▶					▼
Hit hard		Juvenile		Look at	
▶		▼		▼	
Ran away	Molten rock		Animal hide		Hoofed animals
▶	▼		▼		▼
Real beer / Sleek	▶			Lean	
Infor-mation / Craze	▼	Songs-tress	▼	Illness ▶		▼
◣			▼	On the move ▶	
Deadly	By way of / Drink	▶		Discern-ment	Gaze	Gorged
◣		▼		Experi-ments ▶	▼	▼
Open-mouthed	Lass	Intended / Young dog ▶			Move fast
◣	▼		▼	Begin ▶		▼
Napped	A single whole ▶			Regret ▶	
◣			Improve ▶		

155 *Roundword*

Write the answer to each clue in a clockwise direction.
Every solution overlaps the next by either one, two or three letters
and each solution starts in its numbered section. The solution to the
final clue ends with the letter in the first square.

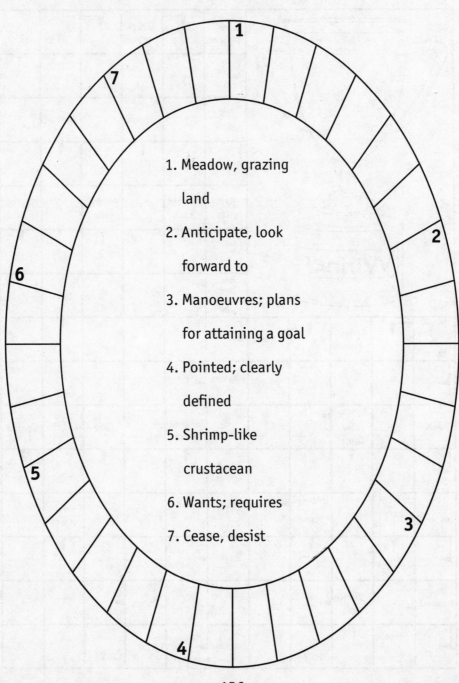

1. Meadow, grazing land
2. Anticipate, look forward to
3. Manoeuvres; plans for attaining a goal
4. Pointed; clearly defined
5. Shrimp-like crustacean
6. Wants; requires
7. Cease, desist

156   Round...

Search for all the 'round' words listed below. Every word can be found in the grid and each runs in a straight, uninterrupted line, either backwards or forwards and either horizontally, diagonally or vertically. All letters except for one must be used.

DOWN
GLOBE
HEAD
ORB
ROBIN
WORLD
WORM

H	E	W	R	W
E	B	O	O	D
A	O	R	B	O
D	L	M	I	W
D	G	I	N	N

---

157   ...and Square

Search for all the 'square' words listed below. Every word can be found in the grid and each runs in a straight, uninterrupted line, either backwards or forwards and either horizontally, diagonally or vertically. All letters except for one must be used.

BASH
BUILT
FOOT
HEEL
LEG
PEG
SAIL
WISE

R	H	S	A	B
F	E	A	U	W
O	E	I	L	I
O	L	L	E	S
T	P	E	G	E

158 Character Assignation

Fill in the Across clues in this crossword in the normal way.
Then read down the diagonal line of eight squares, to reveal:

A character from Rudyard Kipling's *The Jungle Books*:

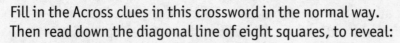

1. Imaginary hero who was no taller than one of the digits on his father's hand (3,4)
2. Part of SW Germany famous for its beer
3. Performing a rôle
4. Turn pink with embarrassment
5. Dull pain
6. Insect which lives in a hive
7. Word introducing an alternative
8. The indefinite article

Character: __ __ __ __ __ __ __ __

159 Logic Puzzle: Hats for Sale

Tammy Shanter has four lovely hats - the ones you see on the shelf below, in fact. Each is of a different colour and has a different coloured ribbon adorning it. Also each was purchased in a different month of last year. Can you discover the facts? We'll take our hats off to you if you can! NB - Hat A is furthest left.

A   B   C   D

1. The yellow hat is immediately next to and right of the green hat.
2. The hat with a purple ribbon is immediately next to the one with a black ribbon.
3. The red hat was bought later in the year than the white hat (which wasn't bought in January). The hat bought in July is further left than the one with a blue ribbon.
4. The red hat is more than one place to the left of the white hat.
5. The hat with a purple ribbon wasn't bought in January, nor is it immediately next to the hat purchased in January.
6. The green hat was bought earlier in the year than the yellow hat, but neither was bought in March.

	Hat colour				Ribbon colour				Month of purchase			
	Green	Red	Yellow	White	Black	Blue	Pink	Purple	January	March	May	July
Hat A												
Hat B												
Hat C												
Hat D												

Hat	Hat colour	Ribbon colour	Month

Across
1. Physical aid (7,4)
7. Writing fluid (3)
9. Green, felt-like fabric (5)
10. Not connected (9)
11. Tsunami (5,4)
12. Deep ravine (5)
13. Pestered (7)
16. Go in (5)
17. Pot (3)
19. Red-breasted bird (5)
21. Playhouse (7)
24. Animated (5)
25. Slide of snow from mountainside (9)
28. Demanding (9)
29. Labours (5)
30. Oxygen, for instance (3)
31. Scandalous (11)

Down
1. Customary (8)
2. Scottish landowner (5)
3. Perfectly, most appropriately (7)
4. Dutch cheese (5)
5. Accord (9)
6. Please (7)
7. Construe (9)
8. Organ in the body (6)
14. Daffodil-like plant (9)
15. Overalls (9)
18. Turnaround (8)
20. Consecrated (7)
22. Pliant (7)
23. Possessing (6)
26. Communion table (5)
27. Principal (5)

Whatever Next?

13	9	12
16	17	19
10	14	10

15	16	19
19	10	9
5	14	13

7	9	15
18	13	12
14	18	14

Which of the following should fill the empty square above?

6	18	16
16	4	12
17	18	13

A

14	10	12
13	18	18
10	12	11

B

10	9	15
14	18	15
15	13	8

C

16	11	12
10	18	12
13	12	17

D

162 *Letter Tracker*

Starting with the A in the top left-hand corner and only moving horizontally or vertically, can you find the fifteen characters from Greek mythology hidden in this box? Each name starts with a letter next to the end of the previous word and they form a continuous line leading to the S in the bottom right-hand corner.

A	E	D	U	S	A	R	C
P	M	S	E	A	N	S	I
H	R	O	L	L	I	S	U
H	S	D	I	C	H	A	S
A	U	R	T	A	N	T	L
D	E	A	E	J	O	S	A
P	S	C	I	A	S	P	A
R	E	T	A	R	O	D	N
O	M	H	E	A	R	M	I
S	I	S	U	S	T	E	S
H	E	E	M	E	E	R	A
C	R	S	D	N	S	S	U
U	L	E	I	O	N	Y	S

163 *Wine & Dine*

Fred's wife took one look at his wine rack and decided that the bottles were a bit grubby - so she dusted them! However, knowing that he likes to place the bottles in a particular order, Fred's wife ran into trouble, since she couldn't quite recall the precise arrangement of the bottles before she'd removed them. She knew each horizontal row and vertical column of the rack held wines of three different types: red, white and rosé from three different countries: England, France and Germany; and in all there are nine different wines in the different combinations, eg there is only one bottle of English rosé, one of French white and one of German red, etc. Can you help Fred's wife to replace the bottles correctly, given the clues below?

In the middle row of the rack, the French wine is further left than the bottle of white wine. In the middle and bottom rows of the rack, the German wine is further left than the French wine. The French rosé is not on the lowest row of the rack.

Left		Right	
1	2	3	Top row
4	5	6	Middle row
7	8	9	Bottom row

In the meantime, blissfully unaware that his wife was dusting his precious bottles of wine, Fred was on his way to his mother's house for lunch. She lives 240 miles away and Fred planned to arrive at exactly 12 noon, which was the precise time that lunch was due to be served.

He set off at ten minutes to eight, allowing himself ten minutes to stop for petrol at a service station that is exactly halfway on the way to his mother's house. He planned to average exactly 60mph, but the first half of his journey included some roadworks and he only managed to average 40mph. He decided it wouldn't matter, since he was exactly half way there, so he would stop for ten minutes as planned and then drive at an average of 80mph for the second half of the journey, thus still arriving in time for lunch.

Despite following this plan precisely and not seeing a single policeman (luckily for him!) on the way, he got a telling off from his mum and a spoilt dinner - why?

164   *Cards on the Table*

What is the face value and suit of each of the cards shown below? Together they total 80. All twelve cards are of different values. In the pack, the values of the cards are as per their numbers and ace = 1, jack = 11, queen = 12 and king = 13. No card is horizontally or vertically next to another of the same colour (hearts and diamonds are red; spades and clubs are black) and there are four different suits in every horizontal row and three different suits in each vertical column.

1. The nine is next to and above the king of spades, which is next to and left of the four.

2. The three is next to and above the ten of diamonds, which is next to and right of the six.

3. Card E has a value two lower than that of card I.

4. Card K has a value one lower than that of card G. Card D has a lower value than that of card J.

5. The ace and queen are of the same suit, which isn't hearts. The three and seven are of the same suit, which isn't spades.

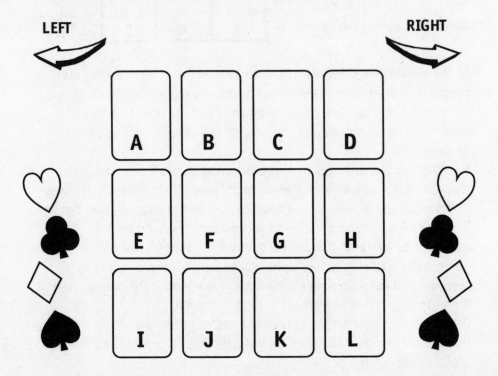

Couplets

The grid below shows a central circle surrounded by shapes, linked to form six sets of three shapes apiece.

Can you place each of the two-letter groups, one per shape, so that every set of three (the central circle, plus the two matching shapes diagonally opposite one another) forms a six-letter word? Whichever pair of letters you place in the central circle will appear in the middle of every word.

TS   EN

FA   UT   SA

KE   RE   VO

DE

PI

YS

UR   UR

Solve the clues and enter the answers in the correspondingly numbered squares. The first letter of each word should be entered immediately above the number and the words can read in either a clockwise or anticlockwise direction. A number of letters have already been entered, to start you on your way.

1. High standing, achieved through success, influence or wealth
2. Bodily protein associated with skin's elasticity
3. Deliberate act of destruction or disruption
4. Showing feelings of unwarranted importance out of overbearing pride
5. Enclosed passageway
6. Overabundance, extreme excess
7. Whole, entire
8. Vocal stress, the relative prominence of a syllable
9. Indefatigable, inexhaustible
10. The body of an aeroplane
11. Amazing occurrences
12. Extremely hungry
13. Fight or struggle
14. Enormous, titanic
15. Fatherly
16. Treachery, especially with regard to aiding an enemy
17. Natural illumination
18. Exhaustive, painstakingly careful and accurate
19. Loathed, despised
20. Beneath the surface of the ocean, submarine
21. Highly seasoned cut of smoked beef
22. The use of an outdated or antiquated word or phrase
23. Average, of no exceptional quality or ability

Figure of Eight

Figure It Out

+ - x

The solutions to the clues are all figures, which should be entered into the grid, crossword-style.

Across
1. A third of 1029
4. 4 Down plus seven
6. 21 squared minus twenty
7. 17 Down doubled
8. 11 Down minus nine
10. 23 Across plus thirty-two
12. 14 Across minus twenty-three
14. 5416 re-arranged
15. Four times 21 Across
17. 6 Across minus four score
19. 1 Across doubled
21. A gross
22. 18 Down trebled
23. 1846 halved

Down
1. 17 Across plus fifteen
2. Four times eighty-five
3. 22 Across times eleven
4. Five times 18 Down
5. A quarter of 948
9. 1515 divided by three
10. 17 Down times three
11. 1132 halved
13. 2 Down minus 186
16. Three times 2371
17. Five times sixty-one
18. 21 Across plus forty-one
19. A third of 1947
20. 221 trebled

168 *Bermuda Triangle*

Travel through the 'Bermuda Triangle' by visiting one room at a time and collecting a letter from each. You can enter the outside passageway as often as you like, but can only visit each room once. When you've completed your tour, rearrange the fifteen letters to spell out a word.

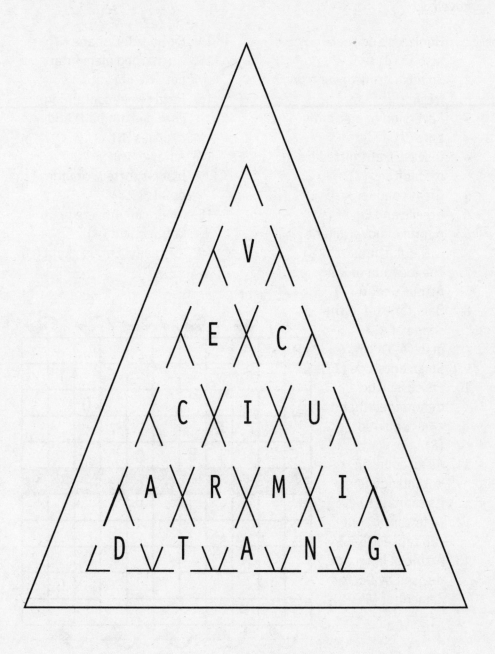

169 Round Tour

The answers to this puzzle form a continuous chain, starting at the top left-hand corner and following the direction indicated by the arrows. The last letter of each word is the first letter of the next and some have already been entered to get you started. When complete, the letters along the shaded row will reveal the name of a well-known novelist.

1. Human gland that secretes insulin (8)
2. Spanish drink of wine and fresh fruit (7)
3. Reversion to a primitive type (7)
4. Disease transmitted by mosquitoes (7)
5. Great conqueror of Greece and Egypt (9)
6. A form of government without a monarch (8)
7. The location of King Arthur's court (7)
8. Beer tankard in the shape of a man (4,3)
9. Small antelope (7)
10. Physicist who determined that e=mc squared (8)
11. Asian country; Kathmandu is its capital (5)
12. Of lettering, not capitalised (5-4)
13. Artificial language devised by Doctor Zamenhof (9)

14. Eight-sided shape (7)
15. Uncharged elementary particle (7)
16. Hard sweet containing chopped almonds and cherries (6)
17. A flower with black-spotted, orange petals (5,4)
18. American university in Connecticut (4)
19. 'Unready' English king (8)

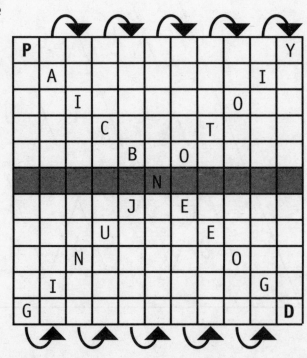

170 Word Ladders

In this puzzle, you need to change one word into another, by altering one letter at a time. However, the positions of each letter must remain unchanged. Here's an example, changing the word TEA to POT:

T	E	A
P	E	A
P	E	T
P	O	T

Now solve these:

G	I	N
A	L	E

I	N	K
P	E	N

W	A	T	E	R
B	L	O	O	D

D	E	A	D
L	I	V	E

171   *What's it Worth?*   ? x ? =

Each symbol stands for a different number. In order to reach the correct total at the end of each row and column, what is the value of a heart, club, diamond and spade, given that each symbol stands for different numbers reading downwards than for reading across?

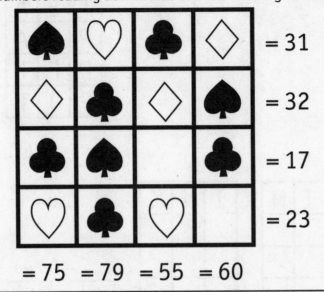

= 31
= 32
= 17
= 23

= 75   = 79   = 55   = 60

---

172   *Summing Up*

$$\begin{array}{r} 1 \\ +\ 2 \\ \times\ 3 \\ -\ 4 \\ \hline 5 \end{array}$$

Arrange one of each of the numbers 2, 4, 7 and 9, as well as one of each of the symbols – (minus), x (times) and + (plus) in every row and column to arrive at the answer at the end of the row or column.

9	–	2	x	4	+	7	=	35
	■		■		■			
							=	24
	■		■		■			
							=	21
	■		■		■			
							=	16
=		=		=		=		■
12		33		31		49		

- 172 -

This one will take a bit of thinking about... The solutions to the Across clues should be entered into the grid in the traditional way, but those to the Down clues should be entered upside down. We've filled in the first, as an example.

Across

1. Relating to the nose (5)
4. The landed estate of a lord (5)
7. Flightless bird (3)
8. Chief magistrate of a district (5)
9. Large cup (3)
10. Rush (5)
13. Dry (wine) (3)
15. Otherwise (4)
17. Foreign (5)
18. Subdue (4)
20. Frosty (3)
22. Supply of something available for future use (5)
25. Epoch (3)
26. Surpass (5)
27. Form of address (3)
28. Tropical lizard (5)
29. Implied (5)

Down

1. Warning signal (5)
2. Board game (5)
3. Part of the foot (4)
4. Run-down, dirty household (4)
5. Citrus fruit (5)
6. Keen (5)
11. Communist nation (5)
12. Meshwork (3)
14. Beer-like beverage (3)
16. Type of lettuce (3)
17. Light mid-afternoon meal (3)
18. Large (5)
19. Deep opening in the Earth's surface (5)
20. Spiny succulent plants (5)
21. Sum total (5)
23. Norway's capital (4)
24. Long and difficult trip (4)

Round the Block

You won't need a starting block to get you under way: because it isn't a race!

Just arrange the 6-letter solutions to the clues into the six blocks around each clue number.

Write the answers in a clockwise direction every time and you'll find that the last answer fits into the first: the main problem will be to decide in which square to put the first letter of each word...

1. Group of six
2. Pill
3. Spanish city
4. Bite off small pieces
5. Flower juice
6. Filter

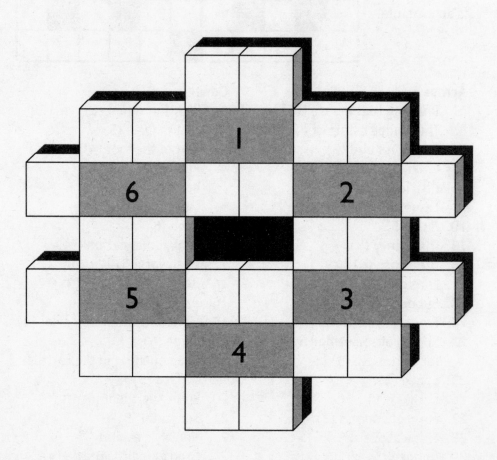

175 *Cryptic Crossword*

Across

1. Unrewarded saint spun around hot joints (9)
7. Untruth by good English lord (5)
8. Reside skilfully after first day (5)
9. Bird that's near can wind (11)
11. Bungling salary cut short by exercise shelter (11)
13. Decorate branch of the armed forces after a party (5)
14. Is Ben turning into a playwright? (5)
16. Kill a point with audible mirth (9)

Down

1. Behold inside brown claw (5)
2. Contrary Greek character becomes consumed (3)
3. Thief's impulse atop man-like construction (11)
4. Jeopardising wrath during finale (11)
5. Observe attendant leaking (7)
6. Artificial pound in cracked safe (5)
10. Lizards decapitated Beck amongst leaves (7)
11. Tire with a reformed note cross (5)
12. Catch up with gold singer (5)
15. Drunkard thus followed by the leader (3)

176 *Loose Vowels*

Every clue in this crossword consists of its solution, with the letters in order, but minus the vowels - gd lck!

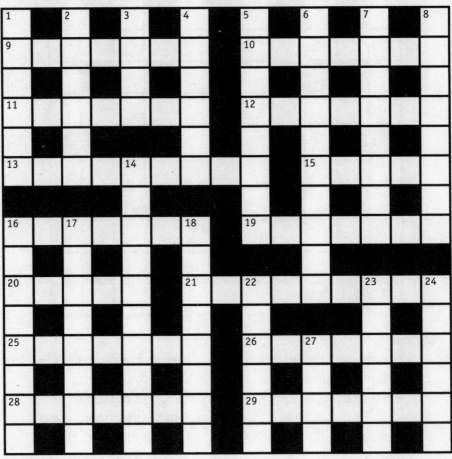

Across

9. GDNG (7)
10. CTT (7)
11. BDMN (7)
12. SCPTR (7)
13. STRNT (9)
15. SDS (5)
16. BRTH (7)
19. RBTL (7)
20. MF (5)
21. BRBCD (9)
25. NCNT (7)
26. SSTN (7)
28. XCT (7)
29. DVL (7)

Down

1. GN (6)
2. BNDT (6)
3. FRM (4)
4. GND (6)
5. FLSTT (8)
6. DFNSBL (10)
7. TSTST (8)
8. RVRSL (8)
14. TRGS (10)
16. BMND (8)
17. FFCTD (8)
18. MBTTR (8)
22. RSD (6)
23. NBL (6)
24. DNR (6)
27. SV (4)

Fill-In

Using the list of words below, can you fill in this crossword?
Every word is used once only and all are required to fill the grid.

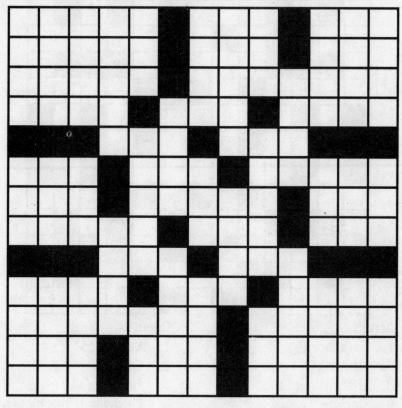

3 Letters
ACE
AGA
ALP
AMP
ARM
ATE
BOB
BRA
EAR
EAT
EBB
EGG
FEN
FLY
ICE

LEO
OAF
OFT
ONE
PER
PRO
PRY
RAG
RIM
SAT
SEA
SET
SPA
TAN
TED
TOY

4 Letters
AMON
ANTI
ARIL
BORE
BRAG
CONE
DAIS
DELI
DOME
EAST
ETNA
ITEM
LYRE
MARE
MEET

NODE
ONCE
OTIS
SCUD
STYE
TEEN
YETI

5 Letters
ACRID
ALIBI
CORAL
DANCE
ERATO
FORCE

LEAPT
MARCH
RABBI
RANGE
RATIO
SCARF
THESE
TOPIC
UNITY

7 Letters
ANALYST
ANEMONE

Coffee Break

Across

1. Carapace (5)
5. Hurled (5)
8. Unit of weight (5)
9. Decide (3)
10. Automaton (5)
11. Cramp (5)
14. Pointed missile (4)
17. Rip (4)
19. Hypersensitive reaction (7)
20. Intentions (4)
21. Bucket (4)
22. White ant (7)
23. Depend (4)
24. Stride (4)
27. Force (5)
30. Garret (5)
32. Employ (3)
33. Young eel (5)
34. Listened (5)
35. First appearance (5)

Down

1. Rebuke (5)
2. Enrol (5)
3. Passing (4)
4. Peruvian tribesman (4)
5. School period (4)
6. Chest bone (3)
7. H_2O (5)
12. Religious traveller (7)
13. Small fish (7)
15. Similar (5)
16. Mouth-watering (5)
17. Varieties (5)
18. Get up (5)
23. Attain (5)
25. Hand digit (5)
26. Pressed fold (5)
27. Frosted (4)
28. Lay slabs (4)
29. Pig fat (4)
31. Popular beverage (3)

179 *Sidewords*

This puzzle can be solved in one of two ways, starting from either the top left corner or the bottom left corner. Can you find the two sequences of words?

Clues starting Top Left

1. Pass, slip away (6)
2. Perennial garden plant (6)
3. Fermentation tanks (4)
4. Long-barrelled firearm (5)
5. Mistakes (6)
6. A shopping centre (4)

Clues starting Bottom Left

1. Animal of the camel family (5)
2. A sailor (3)
3. A cylinder or spool (4)
4. Before anything else (5)
5. Take advantage (5)
6. The Greek underworld (5)
7. Turn white (4)

180   *Trees Company*

Can you fit all of these tree-related words into the grid?

ASH
ELM
GUM
NUT
SAP
YEW

ACER
DEAL
LIME
TEAK
WOOD

ACORN
ASPEN
LEMON
PECAN

BANANA
CATKIN
LAUREL
ORANGE
POPLAR

CYPRESS

181   *Ring-Words*

From the thirty-two segments below, find sixteen 6-letter words, by pairing one set of three letters with another. All of the segments must be used once only.

Ring segments (outer to inner):

ABL, TRY, IRT, LAR, TYP, THI, URY, WIN, FIL, ADV, UPS, POI, TEX, NOW, MIN, AZE, HOT, SUM, HUS, PHY, VOR, SONS, SQU, NTO, RTY, PRO, ERB, FUL, VOR, TRO, LUX, YNX, POS

Answer lines:

_____   _____   _____

_____   _____   _____

_____   _____   _____

_____   _____   _____

_____   _____

182 *Egg-timer*

Can you complete this puzzle in the time it takes to boil an egg?

The answers to the clues are anagrams of the words immediately above and below, plus or minus a letter.

1. Hotel porter
2. Without a pattern
3. Decorate
4. South African currency unit
5. The lowest point
6. Incursion or advance
7. Worshipful

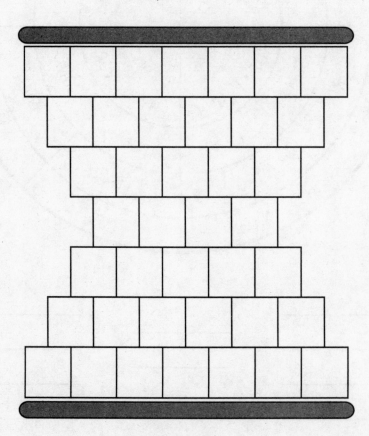

183   *The Pop Quiz*

Fifteen quiz questions to test your knowledge of the world of pop - you'll be top of the pops if you pick fifteen correct answers, of course!

1. For which movie did All Saints record the hit *Pure Shores*?
    (a) *The Beach*   (b) *Titanic*   (c) *Honest*

2. Which boy-band re-recorded Queen's *We Will Rock You* with Brian May and Roger Taylor in 2000?
    (a) *N Sync   (b) A1   (c) Five

3. Who had a No 1 hit with *Don't Call Me Baby*?
    (a) Kylie Minogue   (b) Atomic Kitten   (c) Madison Avenue

4. Which solo star was previously the singer with S-Express?
    (a) Sonique   (b) Heather Small   (c) Gabrielle

5. Which British rock group has a one-armed drummer?
    (a) Saxon   (b) Def Leppard   (c) UFO

6. Who was challenged to a fight by Robbie Williams at the year 2000 Brits?
    (a) Eminem   (b) Liam Gallagher   (c) Gary Barlow

7. Gwen Stefani is the singer with which group?
    (a) No Doubt   (b) Garbage   (c) Sleeper

8. Which rapper has been romantically linked with Jennifer Lopez?
    (a) MC Lyte   (b) Puff Daddy   (c) The Notorious BIG

9. David Coverdale sang with which rock group before forming Whitesnake?
    (a) Deep Purple   (b) Black Sabbath   (c) Pink Floyd

10. Who is the singer with Pulp?
    (a) Damon Albarn   (b) Jarvis Cocker   (c) Richard Ashcroft

11. *Music* was a year 2000 album by which singer?
    (a) Cher   (b) Kate Bush   (c) Madonna

12. Jim Morrison was the singer with which 60s and 70s group?
    (a) The Doors   (b) The Eagles   (c) The Cars

13. *I Try* and *Why Didn't You Call Me* were hits for which singer?
    (a) Macy Gray   (b) Lauryn Hill   (c) Mary J Blige

14. The hits compilation 1 was a smash for which band?
    (a) The Band   (b) The Beatles   (c) The Beach Boys

15. Which Jimi Hendrix hit was written and originally recorded by Bob Dylan?
    (a) *Purple Haze*   (b) *Hey Joe*   (c) *All Along The Watchtower*

184   Simple as A, B, C?   ABC

Each of the small squares in the grid below contains either A, B or C. Every row, column and each of the two long diagonals has exactly two of each letter. The information in the clues refers only to the squares in that row or column. To help you solve this problem, we have given as many clues as we think you will need! Can you tell the letter in each square?

Across:

1. The Cs are adjacent.

2. No two squares containing the same letter are adjacent.

3. The As are further left than the Bs.

6. Each C is immediately next to and to the left of a B.

Down:

1. The Bs are between the As.

2. The As are between the Cs.

3. The Bs are below the As.

5. One B is immediately next to and above a C, whilst the other B is immediately next to and below the other C.

6. Each A is immediately next to and above a C.

	1	2	3	4	5	6
1						
2						
3						
4						
5						
6						

185 *Missing Person*

There are just two words to look for in this wordsearch: CHRISTOPHER and COLUMBUS. One of the letters from the word CHRISTOPHER is shared by the word COLUMBUS - so that the words cross through one another at some point. Explore this grid very carefully - it's not plain sailing!

C	H	R	I	S	T	O	P	H	E	R	C	H	E	R	C
H	R	E	C	O	L	U	M	B	U	S	H	B	U	S	H
R	I	H	C	O	L	U	M	B	C	H	R	B	C	H	R
I	S	P	C	H	C	M	B	U	H	S	I	U	H	S	I
S	T	O	S	O	O	H	R	C	R	U	S	C	R	U	S
T	O	T	M	M	L	I	B	C	I	B	T	C	I	B	T
O	P	S	U	S	U	U	O	H	S	T	O	H	S	T	O
P	H	H	C	O	M	C	M	M	T	H	P	M	T	H	P
H	E	C	U	B	B	H	I	B	O	P	H	B	O	P	H
E	R	C	S	M	U	I	S	U	P	O	E	U	P	O	E
R	C	O	M	U	S	S	T	S	H	S	R	S	H	S	R
C	O	L	B	L	C	T	O	C	U	T	M	C	U	T	C
R	L	U	U	O	O	O	P	B	M	L	O	B	M	L	O
H	E	M	S	C	L	L	M	O	B	O	L	O	B	O	L
R	M	H	C	H	U	U	U	L	U	C	O	L	U	C	I
I	B	C	P	R	L	M	L	U	S	S	M	U	S	S	M
S	U	O	O	O	M	B	S	M	U	O	B	M	U	O	B
T	S	L	C	S	T	U	T	B	B	B	U	B	B	B	U
O	H	U	L	M	S	S	O	U	M	M	S	U	M	M	S
P	C	M	U	B	I	U	I	S	L	U	I	S	L	U	I
H	O	B	M	U	R	I	H	R	C	L	R	R	C	L	R
E	L	S	B	S	H	C	R	C	H	O	H	C	H	O	H
R	O	P	U	S	B	M	U	L	O	C	C	L	O	C	C

186   *Magic Square*

Fill the grid with these letters, forming proper words, so that
1 Across reads the same as 1 Down, 2 Across the same as 2 Down
and 3 Across the same as 3 Down:

D D E E E N N

1	2	3
2		
3		

---

187   *Add a Letter*   *A+B*

Starting with the letter I, add a letter to make first a two-letter word,
then another to make a three-letter word, etc, until you have a
seven-letter word meaning: not yet proven or tested.

---

188   *To Be or Not To Be?*

The question is: can you solve these anagrams, all of which
are works by William Shakespeare?

1. Mean vice thenceforth

2. Oh, vow to free entanglement

3. Shrews find me ivory tower

189   Logic Puzzle: Living Together

Bert, Colin and three other men each live in one of the five houses shown in the diagram below, as do their wives, two of whom are Amy and Ella. The identification letter of each person's house and the initial of each person's name and that of their spouse are three different letters of the alphabet in every case. Can you discover just who lives where?

1. Christine lives directly left of and next door to Edward.

2. Dina lives directly right of and next door to Andy.

3. Beryl lives directly right of and next door to David.

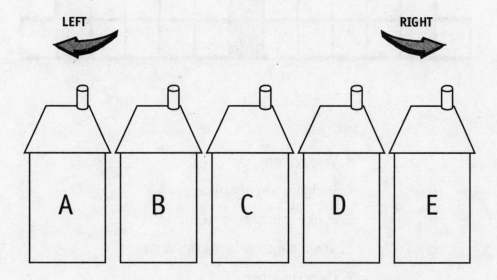

House	Husband	Wife

190 *Pyracross*

Solve the clues to fill in the word on each level of the
pyramid and reveal the hidden word in the central column of bricks.

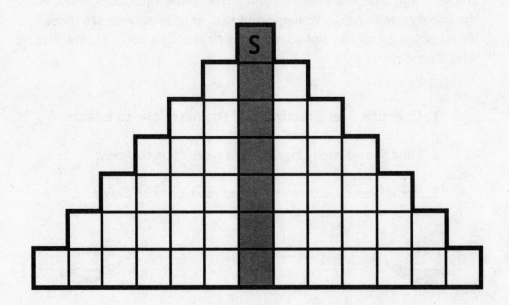

2. Timid

3. Void, vacant

4. Hanging bed of canvas

5. Spoke in hushed tones

6. Green pigment found in plants

7. Living quarters

HIDDEN WORD:_____

Couplets

The grid below shows a central circle surrounded by shapes, linked to form six sets of three shapes apiece.

Can you place each of the two-letter groups, one per shape, so that every set of three (the central circle, plus the two matching shapes diagonally opposite one another) forms a six-letter word? Whichever pair of letters you place in the central circle will appear in the middle of every word.

UE   SU

IT   KI   ND

TA   PU   LE

AE

FO

EM

CA   LY

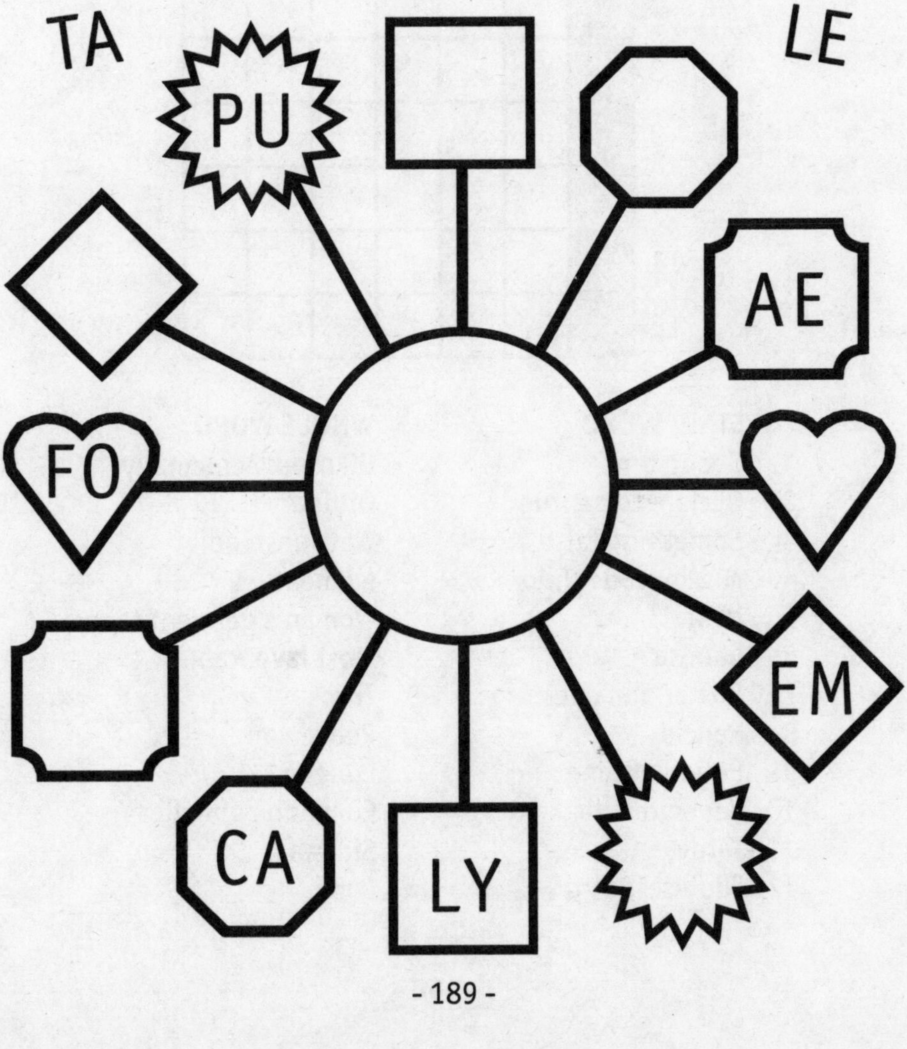

Extensowords

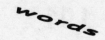

The beginning of each word in this grid is a word in itself, separately clued. When completed, the letters in the shaded vertical column reveal the title of a well-known novel.

	1					
1						
2						
3						
4						
5						
6						
7						
8						
9						
10						
11						
12						

START WORD	WHOLE WORD
1. Set up tent	Oil used medicinally
2. Declare to be true	Ordinary
3. Something false	Walk unsteadily
4. Mischievous child	Momentum
5. Near	Woman's garment (abbr)
6. Choose	Most favourable
7. Roster of names	Turns
8. Rancid	Policeman
9. Period of time	Longed
10. Venomous snake	Common painkiller
11. Tardy	Sideways
12. Flightless bird	Copy

193 *Character Assignation*

Fill in the Across clues in this crossword in the normal way.
Then read down the diagonal line of eight squares, to reveal:

A character from Charles Dickens' *Martin Chuzzlewit*:

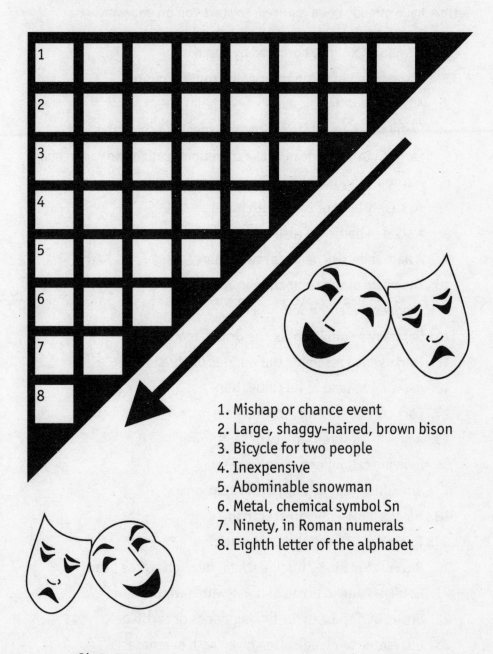

1. Mishap or chance event
2. Large, shaggy-haired, brown bison
3. Bicycle for two people
4. Inexpensive
5. Abominable snowman
6. Metal, chemical symbol Sn
7. Ninety, in Roman numerals
8. Eighth letter of the alphabet

Character: __ __ __ __ __ __ __ __

194   *Figure of Eight*

Solve the clues and enter the answers in the correspondingly numbered squares. The first letter of each word should be entered immediately above the number and the words can read in either a clockwise or anticlockwise direction. A number of letters have already been entered, to start you on your way.

1. European country bordered by Spain

2. Large breed of terrier originally from Yorkshire

3. A tragic or dramatic actor

4. Large ranch or estate in Spanish-speaking countries

5. Large South American snake sometimes called the water-boa

6. A sharp-tongued or bullying old woman

7. To supply land or crops with water

8. A sudden panicked rush by a herd of animals

9. A ball-and-stick game for two teams

10. The name of the submarine in Jules Verne's *Twenty Thousand Leagues Under the Sea*

11. Germany's equivalent of the British motorway

12. Marks which resemble the wounds of Christ

13. Relating to land or its cultivation

14. Cocktail comprising rum and lime juice

15. A green-coloured variety of cauliflower

16. A divine calling or a suitable career

17. An outline or a hypothetical situation

18. Having a pH value greater than 7

19. To scatter in small drops or particles

20. Beverage made by forcing steam through coffee beans

21. Golden-skinned breed of horse with a white mane

22. String of fibrous tissue linking bones or cartilage

23. Guarantee or pledge often given with purchases

Figure of Eight

Figure It Out   + - x

The solutions to the clues are all figures, which should be entered into the grid, crossword-style.

1		2		3		4		5
		6						
7						8	9	
				10		11		
12	13				14			
			15	16				
17		18				19		20
				21				
22						23		

Across

1. Dozen in eleven gross
4. A gross minus a baker's dozen
6. Four times 4 Down
7. 17 Down minus twenty-five
8. 12 Across divided by five
10. Eight times sixty-six
12. Minutes in three days
14. 17 Across times seven
15. 18 Down minus ten
17. Five times 4 Across
19. Twenty-two dozen
21. Hours in nine days
22. Eight times sixty-eight
23. 12 Across divided by eight

Down

1. Four times forty-nine
2. Seconds in four minutes
3. 16 Down plus 248
4. Dozen in nine gross
5. 2 Down minus 106
9. Six times 4 Down
10. 6 Across plus seventy-three
11. 8 Across minus a score
13. 20 Down minus seventy-five
16. Thirty-two squared
17. Five times 125
18. 17 Across minus 131
19. Five times fifty-three
20. Minutes in seven hours

Coffee Break

Across

7. Bewilder (6)
8. Headgear for a horse (6)
9. City in central Italy (8)
10. Irritation (4)
11. Remain (4)
12. Worn out (8)
14. Built-in (8)
17. Preserve (4)
19. Mark left by wound (4)
20. Merited (8)
21. Dog-like (6)
22. Relating to the mountains (6)

Down

1. Vote (6)
2. Disturbance (6)
3. Ms Saunders, comedienne (8)
4. Capable (4)
5. Concealing (6)
6. Trite or obvious remark (6)
13. Lucky charm (8)
15. Flower 'juice' (6)
16. Common garden insect (6)
17. Abrade (6)
18. Capital of Austria (6)
20. Feat (4)

197 *Digital Arrangement*

Can you fit all of the listed numbers into this grid? Any such as 'THIRTY-ONE' should be entered as one continuous word.

ONE	ELEVEN	FIFTY-ONE
TWO	TWELVE	FIFTY-TWO
THREE	FIFTEEN	FIFTY-SEVEN
FOUR	THIRTY	FIFTY-EIGHT
FIVE	THIRTY-ONE	SEVENTY-THREE
SIX	THIRTY-EIGHT	SEVENTY-SEVEN
EIGHT	FORTY	EIGHTY
NINE	FIFTY	NINETY-SIX
TEN		NINETY-EIGHT

198 Round the Block

You won't need a starting block to get you under way:
because it isn't a race!

Just arrange the 6-letter solutions to the clues into the six blocks
around each clue number.

Write the answers in a clockwise direction every time and you'll find
that the last answer fits into the first: the main problem will be to
decide in which square to put the first letter of each word...

1. Package
2. Hit smartly
3. A dealer in fabrics
4. Considerate, not rude
5. Inactive, unchanging
6. Bowl-shaped depression
   in the Earth's surface

199 *Odd One Out*

All of these butterflies share something in common, apart from one - which and why?

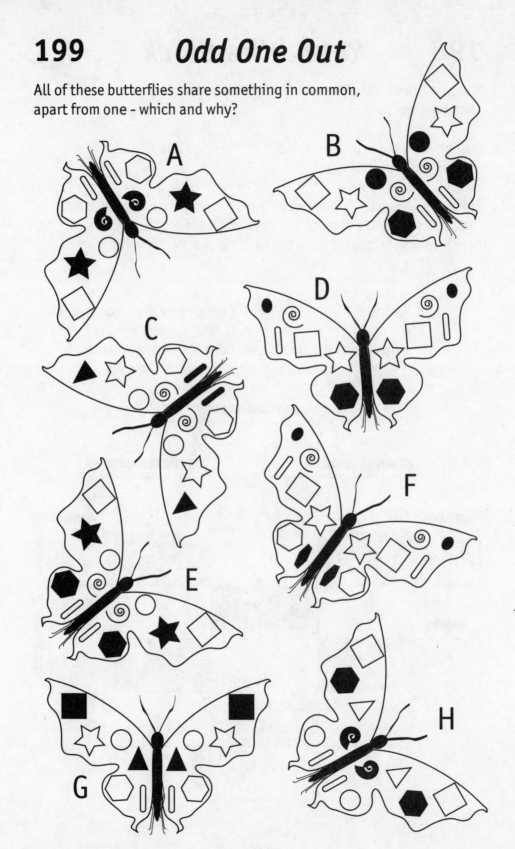

General Knowledge Spiral

Solve the clues in the normal way and enter them into the grid in a clockwise spiral. The last letter of each word is the first letter of the next. When you've finished, the letters in the shaded squares can be rearranged to form the name of a well-known liqueur.

1. The king of the gods, in Greek mythology
2. Alkaline secretion in the mouths of mammals
3. The world's second largest ocean
4. Bone-strengthening substance found in dairy products
5. The planet closest to the Sun in our solar system
6. A language spoken by Jews
7. German-born composer, known for his *Messiah*
8. Retriever dog with a black or golden coat
9. The standard monetary unit of Russia
10. An imaginary line around the Earth
11. European country; capital Bucharest
12. Vegetable also known as the eggplant
13. Surrey town in which the Derby is run
14. Fever transmitted by mosquitoes

HIDDEN WORD: _____

Jigsaw

Fit the jigsaw together to reveal eight animals.

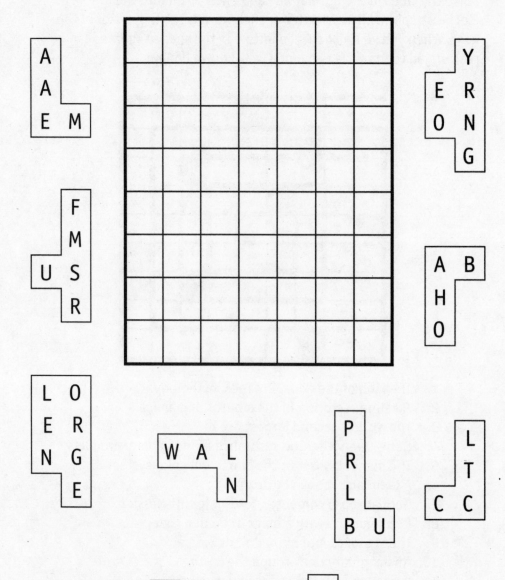

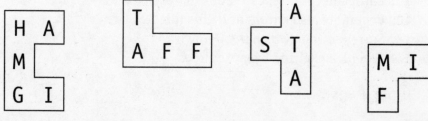

Double Trouble

Solve this one by placing two letters in every square. Each pair of letters reads the same way for both Across and Down words.

Across

1. Move quickly
3. Talk or discourse
5. A chirping insect
7. Blend or circulate
8. Mysterious
9. Lightness of mood
11. Betroth
13. A young woman
15. High-pitched howl
17. A man who courts a woman
19. A kind of star
21. Memorised
22. Wait on
23. Sanctuary
25. Mooring tool
27. Of a sloping type
29. Least colourful
31. Withdraw
33. Spend for profit
35. A ceremonial observance
36. Female ex-pupil
37. Grammatical case
38. More nervous
39. House of a god

Down

1. Bargain
2. Hostility, ill-will
3. Body organ
4. Accuse
5. Picture-house
6. Make wet
10. Admirable quality
12. Opening move
14. Models of excellence
15. Boringly traditional
16. Claim
17. Browning of skin
18. Deliverer of speech
19. Learned authority
20. Eastern language
24. Grope about blindly
26. Selection
28. Recess
29. Eastern temple
30. Endeavour
31. Fastened
32. Distributor of cards
33. Natural, inborn
34. Smother, suppress

203   *Bermuda Triangle*

Travel through the 'Bermuda Triangle' by visiting one room at a time and collecting a letter from each. You can enter the outside passageway as often as you like, but can only visit each room once. When you've completed your tour, rearrange the fifteen letters to spell out a word.

204   *Simple as A, B, C?*   ABC

Each of the small squares in the grid below contains either A, B or C. Every row, column and each of the two long diagonals has exactly two of each letter. The information in the clues refers only to the squares in that row or column. To help you solve this problem, we have given as many clues as we think you will need! Can you tell the letter in each square?

Across:
1. The Bs are between the As.
2. The As are between the Cs.
3. The Cs are adjacent.
4. The Bs are further left than the As.
5. The Bs are further left than the Cs.
6. Each A is immediately to the right of a C.

Down:
2. The As are between the Cs.
3. The Bs are between the As.
5. The As are below the Bs.
6. The As are above the Cs.

	1	2	3	4	5	6
1						
2						
3						
4						
5						
6						

205   *Back and Forth*

This one will take a bit of thinking about... The solutions to the Across clues should be entered into the grid in the traditional way, but those to the Down clues should be entered upside down. We've filled in the first, as an example.

Across
1. Unit of length (5)
4. Foe (5)
7. Writing fluid (3)
8. In front of (5)
9. Similar (5)
11. Remove moisture (3)
12. Black bird (4)
15. Devastate (4)
17. Corpulent (5)
18. Period of time (4)
19. Finest (4)
22. Colour (3)
24. Relating to the countryside (5)
26. Go by car (5)
27. Ancient (3)
28. Fillip (5)
29. Concur (5)

Down
1. Enchant (5)
2. Open and observable (5)
3. Expire (3)
4. Garden tool (4)
5. Anger (3)
6. Destitute (5)
10. Translucent gemstone (5)
11. Great fear (5)
13. Hearing organ (3)
14. Pointed missile (5)
16. Glide over snow (3)
18. Fruit of a tree or bush (5)
20. Bring up (5)
21. Vote into office (5)
23. Lone (4)
25. Neither (3)
26. Sum up (3)

Vowel Movements

The vowels A, E, I, O and U have been removed from the crossword below. Can you replace them correctly? When you have, the first and last letters of every complete word containing an O can be rearranged to form another word.

	R			S	■		■	D
■		■	N			V		
		D		■	S		■	
	T	■			L	■		L
H			R	T	B			T
	■	H		■				■
					L		D	
V			L	S	■		■	
	■	D		T		S	T	

A A A A A A A A A

E E E E E E E E E

I I I I I

O O O

U U U

HIDDEN WORD: _____

Hexagony

Can you place the hexagons into the grid, so that where any triangle touches another along a straight line, the shape in both triangles is the same? No rotation of any hexagon is allowed!

208 *Jigsaw Puzzle*

Which six shapes (three black and three white) can be fitted
together to form the square shown below? The pieces may
be rotated, but not flipped over.

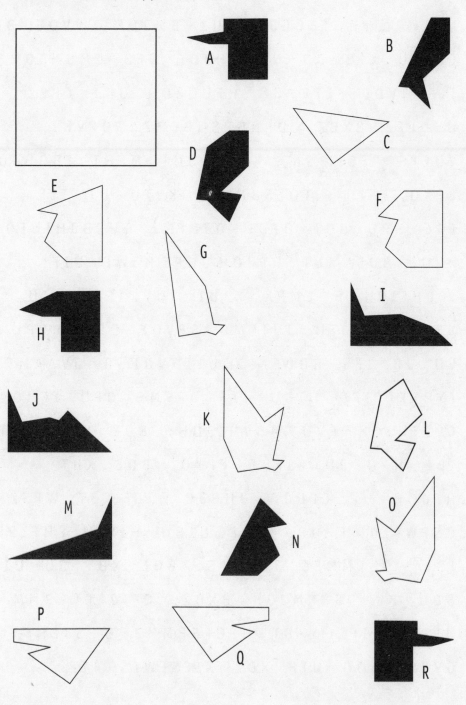

209 The Big Code Breaker

Crack the code to reveal a quotation from Lewis Carroll's
Alice's Adventures in Wonderland.

UIF DIJFG EJGGJDVMUZ BMJDF GPVOE BU

GJSTU XBT JO NBOBHJOH IFS GMBNJOHP:

TIF TVDDFFEFE JO HFUUJOH JUT CPEZ

UVDLFE BXBZ, DPNGPSUBCMZ FOPVHI,

VOEFS IFS BSN, XJUI JUT MFHT IBOHJOH

EPXO, CVU HFOFSBMMZ, KVTU BT TIF

IBE HPU JUT OFDL OJDFMZ TUSBJHIUFOFE

PVU, BOE XBT HPJOH UP HJWF UIF

IFEHFIPH B CMPX XJUI JUT IFBE, JU

XPVME UXJTU JUTFMG SPVOE BOE MPPL

VQ JO IFS GBDF, XJUI TVDI B QVAAMFE

FYQSFTTJPO UIBU TIF DPVME OPU IFMQ

CVSTUJOH PVU MBVHIJOH: BOE XIFO TIF

IBE HPU JUT IFBE EPXO, BOE XBT

HPJOH UP CFHJO BHBJO, JU XBT WFSZ

QSPWPLJOH UP GJOE UIBU UIF IFEHFIPH

IBE VOSPMMFE JUTFMG, BOE XBT JO UIF

BDU PG DSBXMJOH BXBZ: CFTJEFT BMM

UIJT, UIFSF XBT HFOFSBMMZ B SJEHF PS

GVSSPX JO UIF XBZ XIFSFWFS TIF

209 *The Big Code Breaker*

XBOUFE UP TFOE UIF IFHGIPH UP, BOE,

BT UIF EPVCMFE-VQ TPMEJFST XFSF

BMXBZT HFUUJOH VQ BOE XBMLJOH PGG

UP PUIFS QBSUT PG UIF HSPVOE, BMJDF

TPPO DBNF UP UIF DPODMVTJPO UIBU

JU XBT B WFSZ EJGGJDVMU HBNF

JOEFFE. UIF QMBZFST BMM QMBZFE BU

PODF XJUIPVU XBJUJOH GPS UVSOT,

RVBSSFMMJOH BMM UIF XIJMF, BOE

GJHIUJOH GPS UIF IFHHIPHT; BOE JO B

WFSZ TIPSU UJNF UIF RVFFO XBT JO B

GVSJPVT QBTTJPO, BOE XFOU TUBNQJOH

BCPVU, BOE TIPVUJOH "PGG XJUI IJT

IFBE!" PS "PGG XJUI IFS IFBE!" BCPVU

PODF JO B NJOVUF.

A	B	C	D	E	F	G	H

I	J	K	L	M	N	O	P	Q

R	S	T	U	V	W	X	Y	Z

Missing Person

Hidden amongst the letters in the grid below is the name of a famous person from history. The letters of his name can be found reading either backwards or forwards, diagonally, vertically or horizontally, in a straight, uninterrupted line. Who is he?

C	R	B	G	U	L	P	O	Z	A	S	V
H	U	Q	A	C	V	M	C	G	F	A	P
J	S	X	Y	V	S	K	I	W	B	D	F
O	P	T	M	M	I	W	C	F	L	I	U
F	G	K	Q	X	R	Y	L	F	V	R	E
U	H	G	S	D	F	W	C	V	A	B	X
K	J	X	Z	I	R	E	R	J	K	O	L
S	U	B	Z	F	A	C	S	B	F	G	Y
X	Z	P	R	L	N	Y	T	Q	A	V	I
C	O	U	G	S	C	R	C	E	N	K	L
S	P	I	K	B	I	F	G	D	S	O	H
U	I	B	C	F	S	K	J	T	O	H	V
T	G	C	X	P	D	L	F	I	Y	B	I
A	X	Z	K	B	R	Q	S	T	G	F	P
O	I	S	A	V	A	L	X	Z	I	P	D
U	Y	B	Q	O	K	C	J	S	A	T	R
C	V	B	L	K	E	F	G	W	I	P	Z
D	R	T	B	C	V	Z	X	I	O	Q	J
L	P	O	S	W	G	T	J	U	Y	C	X

Coffee Break

Across

1. Result (7)
5. Ciphers (5)
8. At a previous point (7)
9. Scrooge, for example (5)
10. Portly (5)
11. Uncontrived (7)
12. Drink made with beer (6)
14. Forest gods (6)
17. Rambling (7)
19. Burn with steam (5)
22. Effigy (5)
23. Snubbed (7)
24. Glorify (5)
25. Day of the week (7)

Down

1. Conforms (5)
2. Body (5)
3. Left out (7)
4. Mission (6)
5. Heavenly body (5)
6. Demolish (7)
7. More than is needed (7)
12. Small fish (7)
13. US state on the Gulf of Mexico (7)
15. It's said to make the heart grow fonder (7)
16. Self-centered person (6)
18. Torpid (5)
20. Pungent (5)
21. Papa (5)

Figure It Out

The solutions to the clues are all figures, which should be entered into the grid, crossword-style.

Across
1. Four times 198
4. 2 Down plus 132
6. Yards in an eighth of a mile
7. Five times seventy-nine
8. 1248 halved
10. 1 Down plus 196
12. 13 Down times seven
14. 19 Across times five
15. 125 rearranged
17. Four times fifty-three
19. 12 Across divided by seven
21. 19 Down minus three
22. 1662 halved, plus a score
23. 21 Across plus six dozen

Down
1. Three times 15 Across
2. 9 Down minus seventy
3. 32 squared
4. 20 Down doubled
5. Four times 196
9. 7 Across minus a century
10. 23 Across plus thirty-four
11. 10 Across minus eight
13. 5 Down plus forty-seven
16. 12 Across minus 731
17. 482 rearranged
18. 17 Down plus a baker's dozen
19. 1738 halved
20. Six times thirty-three

One for the Pot

Ten teapots were displayed as you see them in the top picture, before Mrs Jones came into the shop and bought one. However, since she picked them all up to look at them very carefully before making her choice and then replaced them in a different order, we aren't sure exactly which one Mrs Jones eventually purchased. Can you decide?

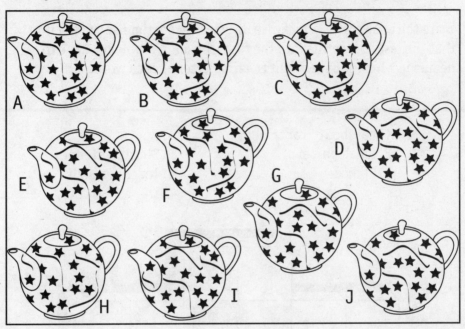

214 Round the Block

You won't need a starting block to get you under way: because it isn't a race!

Just arrange the 6-letter solutions to the clues into the six blocks around each clue number.

Write the answers in a clockwise direction every time and you'll find that the last answer fits into the first: the main problem will be to decide in which square to put the first letter of each word...

1. Cardboard container
2. Small parcel
3. Choice

4. Ape
5. Shortsightedness
6. Teaches a skill

Filling in Time

Can you fit twenty four of the listed words into the crossword?
Take care   six of these words don't actually belong in the grid!

COST	ABLAZE	APPARENT
GRIN	ANGLER	BRIGHTEN
RAYS	DOCTOR	DINOSAUR
SEAL	EVOLVE	SERVICED
TOFU	INDOOR	UNGLAZED

ALLOT	AFRICAN	EXTRAVAGANZA
INCUR	AIRPORT	INTERROGATOR
ONION	APRICOT	NATURALISING
REIGN	OPENING	NEIGHBOURING
TARRY	RELAXED	OUTMANOEUVRE

Figure of Eight

Solve the clues and enter the answers in the correspondingly numbered squares. The first letter of each word should be entered immediately above the number and the words can read in either a clockwise or anticlockwise direction. A number of letters have already been entered, to start you on your way.

1. All the gods of a religion
2. Microscopic forms of organic life that float in the sea or fresh water
3. The Scottish name for New Year's Eve
4. A large sword once used by Scottish Highlanders
5. Delicate and ornamental lacework of gold or silver
6. A round-backed instrument similar to the lute
7. Surname of TV presenter Clive and actress Gillian
8. Sea that lies between the Azores and the West Indies
9. The scientific study of soil as it relates to crop production
10. Widely-grown shrub the leaves of which are used in cooking and perfumery
11. The degree of a slope as compared to the horizontal
12. American state of which Dover is the capital
13. Thorny shrub on which may blossom grows
14. Person who rakes in and pays out money at a gambling table
15. Bacterium sometimes found in under-cooked chicken
16. A small bushy-tailed American monkey
17. A dry brandy made in SW France
18. A lively Spanish dance for two, involving castanets
19. An aromatic herb used in vinegar and sauces
20. A member of an ancient Jewish sect
21. The capital and largest city of Belgium
22. Greek god of wine and fertility, sometimes called Bacchus
23. Delusions of persecution or pursuit

Figure of Eight

Globetrotters

BRIAN, DECLAN, MAURICE, SANDRA, MARGE, CORA, STEWART, SUSIE, MICK, JANE, ELAINE, GLENDA, TERESA, WALTER, GRANT, RUPERT, GILLIAN, LINDA, LORENZO, GUS, FELICITY, MANDY, SADIE and ARTHUR all work for a company with offices in various countries across the globe. Use the letters of their names to fill the spaces below and thus reveal these countries:

```
            __ __ __ T __
          __ R __ __ __ __
        P __ __ T __ __ __ __
          __ P __ __ __ __
      __ __ __ __ __ L __ __ __ __
      __ __ __ __ __ A __ __ __
      A __ __ __ __ __ __
          __ T __ __ __
        __ __ __ __ __ __ Y
      I __ __ __ __ __ __
    __ C __ __ __ __ __
      __ __ __ __ __ E __
      __ U __ __ __ __
    __ H __ __ __ __ __
      I __ D __ __ __
      __ __ X __ __ __
    B __ __ __ __ __ __
      __ __ __ N __ __
        __ A __ __ __
    A __ __ __ __ __ __
      __ __ S __ __ __
  __ __ __ __ __ __ __ A __ __ S
    __ __ I __ __ __ __ __ __ __
```

Box Clever

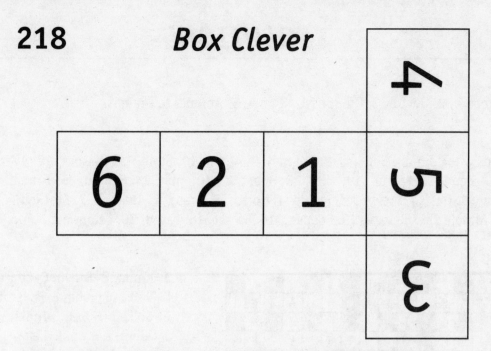

When the above is folded to form a cube, just one of the following can be produced. Which one?

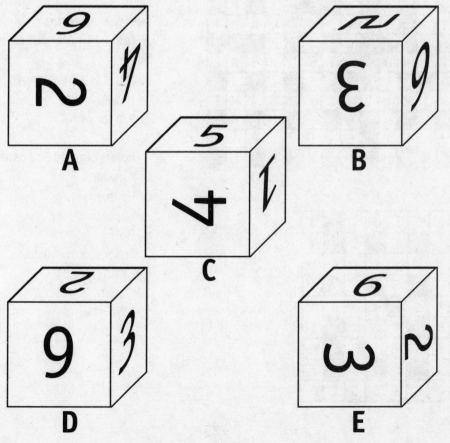

A

B

C

D

E

1

1. Record, 2. Doctor, 3. Dragon, 4. Normal, 5. Animal, 6. Dramas.

2

Across: 1. Opinion, 5. Glass, 8. Snippet, 9. Alpha, 10. Style, 11. Cassock, 12. Averse, 14. Ascend, 17. Fretful, 19. Sifts, 22. Boast, 23. Gremlin, 24. Emend, 25. Titanic.
Down: 1. Oasis, 2. Icily, 3. Impress, 4. Notice, 5. Grass, 6. Approve, 7. Stacked, 12. Affable, 13. Elevate, 15. Suspect, 16. Blight, 18. Fated, 20. Felon, 21. Sonic.

3

```
W   R   H   F   S   G       E
B A S E B A L L   Q U A I N T
  X   C   T   A   U   Z   V
B I E R   C A N T I L E V E R
  N   E   H   N       E   L
A G R A R I A N   T Y C O O N
    T   N   A       A     P
F I J I   G I V E N   C H E F
  N   V     E   I   K     F
O F F E N D   L Y N C H I N G
  L     E     E   A     I
S E N S U A L I S T   N A M E
  X   E   R   N   E   D   B
R E J E C T   C L E V E R L Y
  D   K   H   H   N   D   E
```

4

A=Alpha, B=Bravo, C=Charlie, D=Delta, E=Echo, F=Foxtrot, G=Golf, H=Hotel, I=India, J=Juliet, K=Kilo, L=Lima, M=Mike, N=November, O=Oscar, P=Papa, Q=Quebec, R=Romeo, S=Sierra, T=Tango, U=Uniform, V=Victor, W=Whisky, X=X-ray, Y=Yankee and Z=Zulu.

Thus:

1. Doris is a name not represented
2. November
3. India
4. Peru (Lima is the capital)
5. Quebec
6. Uniform
7. Papa
8. Golf
9. Foxtrot and tango
10. Kilo
11. Echo
12. Whisky

5

```
A M A T E U R   U
S   P   A   E   N
S   A R S E N A L
I   R   E   O   E
D A T A   A U R A
U   H   A   N   S
O C E A N I C   H
U   I   T   E   E
S   D R E S S E D
```

The hidden word is ACROSS.

SOLUTIONS

6

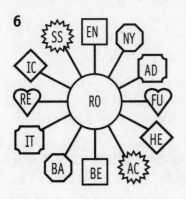

7

Brick O=53 and O=M+N. K=14, so M=J+14 and N=14+L, so 53=J+14+14+L, thus 25=J+L. J=8+G and L=H+I, so 17=G+H+I. 14=G+H (K), so I=3. D is 1 or 2. 14=G+H (K) and G=B+4. H=4+D, so 14=B+4+4+D and 6=B+D. B isn't 4 (intro), so D isn't 2. Thus D=1 and E=2 (I). H=5, L=8, N=22, M=31, J=17, G=9, B=5 and A=3.
Thus:
A=3, B=5, C=4, D=1, E=2, F=8, G=9, H=5, I=3, J=17, K=14, L=8, M=31, N=22, O=53.

8

The difference between the sum of both diagonals in each case is equal to the centre value.
Thus the missing letter is X.

9

Here's one way
(and reflections and
rotations will also work)

6	14	7
10	9	8
11	4	12

10

O, no (or on), won (or now, or own), down, endow (or owned), wonder, drowned.

11

1. *A Christmas Carol*; 2. *A Tale of Two Cities*;
3. *David Copperfield*.

12

M	F	U	G	N	I	H	C	T
O		F						I
I		A	R	E	V	E		M
S		W	A			S		I
T		E	L			P		L
U		S	E			A		A
R		T	R	T		L		E
E		R				E		R
C		U	C	K	E	R	N	E
E								H
D	E	C	A	G	O	N	S	E	T

13

Anchor, Astern, Funnel, Galley, Jetsam, Launch, Mizzen, Rudder, Splice, Tiller.

14

```
C A U T I O N ▪ C Y A N I D E
L . S . N . O . U . R . R . L
A P H I D ▪ S U B S C R I B E
M . E . E . E . I . ▪ . S . M
O A R ▪ X E B E C ▪ O C H R E
U . E . L . ▪ . C . ▪ . E . N
R A T I O ▪ E F F I C I E N T
. . T . D . E . A . U . N . .
A D E N O I D A L ▪ R I N S E
U . U . ▪ . U . S . O . L . .
C E D A R ▪ S C E N E ▪ B E E
T . U . ▪ . H . H . L . L . C
I N C O G N I T O ▪ I D I O T
O . A . O . R . O . T . N . O
N E T W O R K ▪ D R E D G E R
```

15

A. 56 - 1x2, 2x3, 3x4, 4x5, etc.
B. 21 - each is the sum of the previous two.
C. 6 - each is the number of letters in the digit written as a word.
D. 56 - each is the square of its position, plus 7.
E. 10,368 - alternately multiply and add the last two numbers, eg 1x1, 2+2, 2x4, 4+8, etc.
F. 63 - 0x2, 1x3, 2x4, 3x5, etc.
G. 31 - these are the numbers of days in the months of the year.
H. 29/30 - the top is the difference between the two previous (upper/lower) numbers and the bottom is a multiple of the two.

16

1. Grid, 2. Amble, 3. Broken, 4. Radical, 5. Imminent, 6. Excavator, 7. Locomotive, 8. Loudspeaker, 9. Eavesdropper.
Hidden pop singer: GABRIELLE

17

1. Athens, Dublin, Moscow.
2. Ankara, London, Prague.
3. Ottawa, Peking, Saigon.
4. Beirut, Lisbon, Manila.
Hidden name: ERIC

18

```
▪ U ▪ B ▪ B ▪ A ▪ A ▪ W ▪
E N V I R O N M E N T A L
▪ I ▪ S ▪ O ▪ B ▪ G ▪ T ▪ L
A N A E S T H E T I S E D
▪ H ▪ C ▪ L ▪ R ▪ N ▪ R ▪
C A N T E E N ▪ H A P P Y
▪ B ▪ G ▪ C ▪ ▪ ▪ R ▪
C I V I C ▪ P H A E T O N
▪ T ▪ N ▪ C ▪ I ▪ X ▪ O ▪
H A N D K E R C H I E F S
▪ B ▪ O ▪ L ▪ A ▪ S ▪ I ▪
F L O O D L I G H T I N G
▪ E ▪ R ▪ O ▪ O ▪ S ▪ G ▪
```

19

5	x	3	−	8	+	6	=	13
+		x		−		−		
8	−	6	+	3	x	5	=	25
−		+		x		+		
3	+	5	x	6	−	8	=	40
x		−		+		x		
6	x	8	−	5	+	3	=	46
=		=		=		=		
60		15		35		27		

SOLUTIONS

20

1. Sir Cliff Richard; 2. John Wayne; 3. Doris Day; 4. Pelé; 5. Barbara Stanwyck; 6. Elton John; 7. Jordan; 8. Alice Cooper; 9. Billy Idol; 10. Demi Moore.

21

Groucho Marx: I find television very educating. Every time somebody turns on the set, I go into the other room and read a book.

22

The flat in Rugby is £45,000 (clue 2) and the one in Hayes is £90,000 (clue 3). Laura's flat cost £70,000 (4). Darren's in Ayr (1) thus cost £40,000 and Deborah's flat is £35,000. Laura isn't moving to Kendal (4), so Rhyll. By elimination, Deborah is going to Kendal. Keith isn't going to Rugby (2), so Hayes. George is moving to Rugby.

Thus:

Darren Ayr £40,000;
Deborah Kendal £35,000;
George Rugby £45,000;
Keith Hayes £90,000;
Laura Rhyll £70,000.

23

1. Turmoil, 2. Illegal, 3. Gallon, 4. Onerous, 5. Useless, 6. Salad, 7. Adroit.

24

Here are just a few of the words you could have made:
Awe, Awed, Daw, Dew, Draw, Drew, Raw, Saw, Sawed, Sew, Stew, Steward, Straw, Strew, Swat, Swear, Sweat, Taw, Trews, Wad, Wade, Wader, War, Ward, Wart, Was, Waste, Wasted, Waster, Water, Wear, Wed, West, Wet.

25

A	N	G	L	E	S	E	Y
A	L	D	E	R	N	E	Y
T	R	I	N	I	D	A	D
T	A	S	M	A	N	I	A
R	O	T	H	E	S	A	Y
D	O	M	I	N	I	C	A
M	A	L	L	O	R	C	A
G	U	E	R	N	S	E	Y

26

6	1	3	2	3	9
8	4	1	5	6	8
7	6	5	9	8	4
6	5	4	3	2	1
7	2	9	2	4	7
1	3	7	8	5	9

SOLUTIONS

27

Across: 1. Bambi, 3. Gilbert, 6. Squares, 8. Asian, 10. Birdwatcher, 12. Pail, 13. Greek, 15. Itch, 17. Promenaders, 19. Early, 20. Bronzed, 21. Harness, 22. Scowl.
Down: 1. Bishop, 2. Brazil, 3. Gas, 4. Basic, 5. Tundra, 7. Enduring, 9. Calendar, 10. Bingo, 11. Halts, 14. Speech, 15. Ironic, 16. Handel, 18. Melon, 20. Bus.

28

Flurry, Furrow, Horror, Hyssop, Insult, Knight, Lowest, Nymphs, Oozing, Rhythm, Smoggy, Sphinx, Throng, Thrown, Twists, Within.

29

The 'y' of 'Birthday' has changed colour; the furthest left balloon is missing a dot; the largest present is missing a bow; one of the candles on the cake has changed colour; one star on the cake has changed colour; one heart on the cake has changed colour; and a streamer (on the right) has changed colour.

30

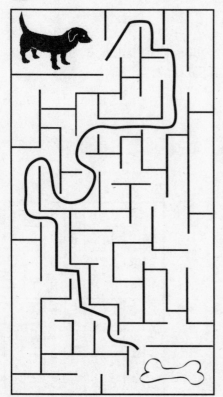

31

A=7, B=6, C=4, D=6, E=8
Thus: PHENOMENON

32

Across: 1. Factor, 4. Catnip, 9. Eliza, 10. Obverse, 11. Reptile, 12. Coati, 13. Denmark Strait, 15. Crawl, 16. Assegai, 18. Leeds, 20. Erasmus, 21. Ravioli, 22. Slang, 25. Thunder, 27. Ernie, 28. The Bard of Avon, 31. Ultra, 32. Salerno, 34. Landing, 35. Thant, 36. Ecarté, 37. Enzyme.
Down: 1. Free radical, 2. Chippendale, 3. Omani, 5. Advocates, 6. Nirvana, 7. Paediatrics, 8. Kopeck, 14. Atlas, 16. Atelier, 17. Easel, 19. Djinn, 21. Ratatouille, 22. Sheaf, 23. Anniversary, 24. Greenbottle, 26. Dramatist, 29. Estonia, 30. Design, 33. Latin.

SOLUTIONS

33

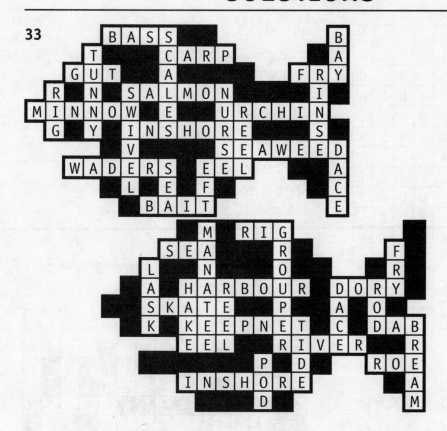

34

Heart=2, club=6, diamond=4, spade=12.
Four circles are needed to balance scale C. Reading across scale A, the values are
Cross=6, Circle=2, Cylinder=3 and Arrow=1.

35

The A is 3 (clues 1 and 3). L is 19 (7 and 8), I is 24 (4 and 8) and U is 5 (3 and 8), so Q is
22 (8). E is 2 (1 and 6), C is 6 (1 and 4), T is 4 (1 and 7) and O is 7 (1 and 5), so V is 1
(1). R is 9 (3 and 6) and G is 15 (4 and 6), so J is 8 (6). S is 13 (5 and 7), so K is 20 (7).
B is 14 (2 and 3) and D is 23 (3 and 4), so Z is 16 (3). W is 21 (4 and 5), N is 11 (2 and
4), X is 25 (4), M is 12 (2), H is 18 (5 and 9), P is 17 (5). Y is 10 (9) and there is only one
remaining letter, F, which is therefore 26.
Thus:
1=V, 2=E, 3=A, 4=T, 5=U, 6=C, 7=O, 8=J, 9=R, 10=Y, 11=N, 12=M, 13=S, 14=B, 15=G,
16=Z, 17=P, 18=H, 19=L, 20=K, 21=W, 22=Q, 23=D, 24=I, 25=X, 26=F.

SOLUTIONS

36

```
    N   L
  B E H O L D
  A   N   O
  D R A G O N
    M   D
  R W A N D A
  A T E   V
A B   F I E R C E
D R O O P T U D O R
E   M A Y   R   L
R A B B I   C I G A R
  A   N O R S E   U
M E R I T   A H E A D
  O   R E S T   S I D
I N T E R   E V E R Y
```

37

1. Saigon, 2. Narcissus, 3. Stockholm,
4. Magnum, 5. Meridian, 6. Neptune,
7. Edelweiss, 8. Sanskrit, 9. Tanner,
10. Rembrandt, 11. Truman, 12. Nectarine
Hidden word: ALGERIA.

38

Starting top left:
1. Enable, 2. Gnat, 3. Set, 4. Tastes,
5. Saturn, 6. Acetic.
Starting bottom left:
1. Cite, 2. Can, 3. Rut, 4. Assets, 5. Attest,
6. Angel, 7. Bane.

39

```
A C M E ▓ B L U E S ▓ C U T E
P ▓ L E O ▓ T ▓ P ▓ N ▓ N
S C A B ▓ G A T E A U ▓ I ▓ V
E ▓ O ▓ U ▓ E ▓ N U T T Y
▓ A W E S T R U C K ▓ O ▓
D U D ▓ M ▓ R ▓ K ▓ I N A N E
O ▓ J ▓ P R O T E I N ▓ M ▓ G
S A U N A ▓ J ▓ L ▓ D I A R Y
E ▓ S ▓ T R A P E Z E ▓ Z ▓ P
D I T C H ▓ N ▓ L ▓ S ▓ E F T
▓ N ▓ I N S P E C T E D ▓
U N C L E ▓ A ▓ U ▓ I ▓ Y
P ▓ A ▓ S I S T E R ▓ D O Z E
O ▓ L ▓ R ▓ C ▓ E K E ▓ L
N A M E ▓ E T H O S ▓ R E E L
```

40

Oliver Cromwell

```
D C L A U J P O T Y S S
D T Q A C V M H G F A P
I S X Y V S P I W B D F
S O T M W F W C A L I U
R G K Q X R Y L L L R E
A H G S D E W C V L B G
E J X Z I L E R J E O L
L U B V F A C S B W G Y
X Z P R L N Y T Q M V I
R O U G S C R C E O K T
C P I K B J F G D R O L
U J B C F K O I T C P V
T G H C E S L F I R B I
A M D K B R Q S T E F S
L I S A V A L X Z V P K
U Y B Q O L C J S I T R
L V B L K E F G W L P M
D R T A C V Z X I O Q J
F P O S M O T J D E C O
```

41

1. RouBle, 2. CoUple, 3. LadDer, 4. DeGree,
5. BreEze, 6. FaTter.
Thus - BUDGET.

SOLUTIONS

42

1. Charm, 2. Mead, 3. Dearest, 4. Trowel, 5. Loop, 6. Postman, 7. North, 8. Harbour, 9. Rhinoceros, 10. Steal, 11. Leaps, 12. Shore, 13. Edited.
Mode of transport: MOTOR CAR

43

Across: 1. Cobra, 4. Chart, 7. Nearly, 8. Halo, 10. Thwarting, 11. Alignment, 14. Iraq, 15. Feeble, 16. Noted, 17. Tools.
Down: 1. Consolation, 2. Beast, 3. Allowing, 5. Abaci, 6. Thoughtless, 9. Briefest, 12. Inapt, 13. Taboo.

44

C

46

Extraordinarily

47

1. Alligator, 2. Boomerang,
3. Withdrawn, 4. Sincerity,
5. Sideboard, 6. Shuddered,
7. Timetable, 8. Turbulent,
9. Xylophone.

45

3	8	4	2	1	9	6	7	5
5	1	7	8	3	6	9	2	4
2	6	9	7	5	4	1	3	8
4	5	2	3	9	1	8	6	7
1	9	6	4	8	7	3	5	2
7	3	8	6	2	5	4	9	1
6	2	5	9	4	8	7	1	3
9	4	1	5	7	3	2	8	6
8	7	3	1	6	2	5	4	9

48

Across: 1. Zebra, 3. Acerbic, 6. Athlete, 8. Abate, 10. Featureless, 12. Turf, 13. Meant, 15. Cede, 17. Battlefield, 19. Choke, 20. Whistle, 21. Scenery, 22. Aroma.
Down: 1. Zealot, 2. Relief, 3. Ace, 4. Rebel, 5. Cheese, 7. Tattered, 9. Brandish, 10. Frost, 11. Erred, 14. Abacus, 15. Closer, 16. Eczema, 18. Token, 20. Way.

49

L	L	A	M	A
L	I	B	E	L
A	B	A	T	E
M	E	T	E	R
A	L	E	R	T

P	R	A	N	G
R	A	D	I	O
A	D	D	E	R
N	I	E	C	E
G	O	R	E	D

50

Cards total 87 (intro), so the 4 is missing. Card L is a diamond (clue 5), so B is also a diamond (intro) and D and J are hearts. The king isn't C (clue 1) and the queen isn't J (7), so card A is the king of clubs (2) and E is the queen of hearts. F isn't a spade (2), so club; thus C is a spade, G a diamond, H a spade, I a spade and K a club (intro). The ace (value one) isn't F or H (1), so is card G (4). In clue 7, either I, J and K have values of 2, 3 and/or 8; or I, J and K have values of 2, 5 and/or 6. Thus the 2 is either I, J or K. If I, J and K are 2, 3 and/or 8, then (1) C=6, H=7 and F=9, leaving nowhere for the jack (value 11) (3 and 5). Thus I, J and K have values of 2, 5 and/or 6. By elimination, C, H and F have values of either 7, 8 and/or 10 (1), or 8, 9 and/or 11. Thus the 8 is either C or H. Card D has an even-numbered value (3), so is the 10. Thus card C is the 8, F is the jack (1) and H is the 9. The 3 isn't card B (6), so L. K is the 5 and I the 6 (6), so J is the 2. Card B is the 7.

Thus:

KC	7D	8S	10H
QH	JC	AD	9S
6S	2H	5C	3D

51

D

52

PIG-big-bag-bay-say-STY;
DATA-date-dare-dire-dirk-DISK;
SOFT-sort-port-part-hart-HARD;
READ-road-rood-rook-BOOK.

53

5	6	2	3	1	4
2	3	4	1	5	6
4	1	3	5	6	2
6	2	1	4	3	5
1	4	5	6	2	3
3	5	6	2	4	1

54

R	U	B	B	I	S	H		D	E	N	S	E
E		O		G		O				I		T
C	A	R	O	L		P	A	N	A	C	H	E
U		E		O		L		E		E		R
R	O	D	E	O	S		B	A	R	R	E	N
		O		E		U						A
T	E	M	P	E	R	A	M	E	N	T	A	L
O			P		E		A					L
R	E	D	U	C	E		N	I	M	B	L	E
M			R		N		N		L		V	
E	X	E	C	U	T	E		A	R	O	M	A
N			A		G		N		I		A	D
T	E	D	D	Y		O	V	E	R	D	U	E

55

Hidden TV personality: CILLA BLACK

SECT   CASTE   CASKET

NEAT   ENACT   LANCET

RISE   CRIES   SLICER

DREG   RIDGE   GIRDLE

LEST   TALES   STABLE

56

Here are just a few of the words you could have made: Ail, Aim, Alp, Amp, Amplify, Fail, Flam, Flap, Flay, Lam, Lamp, Lap, Lay, Mail, Map, May, Pail, Pal, Palm, Pay, Play, Yam, Yap.

57

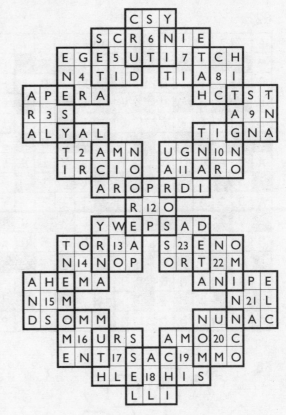

58

59

9 (x3=) 27 (-20=) 7 (x4=) 28 (-20=) 8 (x5=) 40
Thus: (40-20) the value of S=20

60

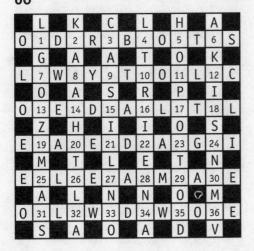

61

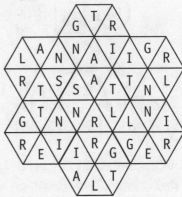

SOLUTIONS

62

A	Z	A	L	E	A		P	A	C	I	F	I	S	T
M		M		A		C		R		R		R		P
B	O	U	T	I	Q	U	E		V	I	O	L	E	T
L		H		U		V		E		S		C		
E	X	P	E	R	I	M	E	N	T		T	W	I	N
		E		E		N			B			A		
A	B	A	C	U	S		T	E	R	R	I	B	L	E
	O		E		C		E		T		T		L	
A	D	J	A	C	E	N	T		T	I	E	D	Y	E
	Y		S		N		E		E		U			
O	G	R	E		C	H	A	I	N	S	M	O	K	E
	U		F		R		R		T		A			C
J	A	W	I	N	G		O	R	I	G	I	N	A	L
	R		R		E		O		V		Z			A
A	D	D	E	N	D	U	M		E	X	E	M	P	T

63

Badger, Choppy, Closer, Elixir, Exhort, Frisky, Govern, Guzzle, Hurtle, Influx, Rhymes, Sheikh, Shrine, Soothe, Wimple, Wooded.

64

A: Each smaller shape makes a quarter turn anticlockwise every time.

65

The hidden word is: COATED

A	N	A	L	O	G	I	S	T
R		I		V		A		
I	S	R	A	E	L	I	T	E
S		E		R			E	
E	A	R	T	H	I	E	S	T
	U		E		L		A	
E	G	O	M	A	N	I	A	C
	U		R		T		T	I
G	R	E	E	D	I	E	S	T

66

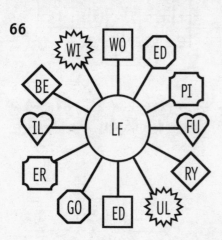

67

From clues 1 and 2, B=2, I=4 and Y=16. U=8 (clue 14). W is either 3 or 5 (6), as is Q (10), so (4) T=15. Z is either 9 or 25 (6), as is C (10). In clue 13, M=6 and R=20. F isn't 7 (9), so 1. In clue 12, S and E are either 7 and/or 13, so H=23 (15) and C=25; thus Z=9 (6), W=3 and (10) Q=5. In clue 9, P is either 22 or 24 and O is either 11 or 12. So (3) J is either 17 or 18. So (16) J=18 and K=10. O=12 (3). P=24 (9). L=17 and E=7 (11), so (12) S=13. G=21 and A=11 (7). X=26 and V=22 (5). N=19 and D=14 (8). Thus:

A=11; B=2; C=25; D=14; E=7; F=1; G=21; H=23; I=4; J=18; K=10; L=17; M=6; N=19; O=12; P=24; Q=5; R=20; S=13; T=15; U=8; V=22; W=3; X=26; Y=16; Z=9.

SOLUTIONS

68

Across: 1. Thyme, 4. Cairo, 7. Via, 8. Pause, 9. Melon, 10. Nee, 11. Right, 14. Large, 17. Deter, 20. Belly, 23. Ire, 24. Tanks, 25. Rinse, 26. Key, 27. Hurry, 28. Lurid.
Down: 1. Taper, 2. Young, 3. Event, 4. Camel, 5. Idler, 6. Ounce, 12. Ice, 13. Hoe, 15. Awe, 16. Gel, 17. Dutch, 18. Tenor, 19. Risky, 20. Beryl, 21. Liner, 22. Yield.
Across: 1. Carol, 4. Cause, 7. Ado, 8. Rugby, 9. Medal, 10. Bee, 11. Enemy, 14. Treat, 17. Sword, 20. Adept, 23. Rue, 24. Igloo, 25. Scrap, 26. Leo, 27. Tidal, 28. Perry.
Down: 1. Carve, 2. Rogue, 3. Lay-by, 4. Comet, 5. Undue, 6. Eclat, 12. New, 13. Mar, 15. Red, 16. Asp, 17. Saint, 18. Oiled, 19. Droll, 20. Aesop, 21. Error, 22. Tipsy.

69

Heaven Sent which got 5 stars wasn't written by Geoff (clue 1), Clive or Cindy (clue 2) or Louise (3), so Margo. *Danger Money* didn't get 4 stars (4), so wasn't written by Cindy (2). Nor was it written by Louise (3) or Geoff (4), so Clive. It got either one or 2 stars and Cindy's got either 3 or 4 (2). Louise's also got either one or 2 stars (3), so Geoff's got 3 or 4. *Milestone* was given either 3 or 4 stars (3) and wasn't written by Cindy, so Geoff. Thus (4) it got 3 stars and Clive's book got 2. Louise's got one star. Cindy's book got 4 stars, thus (2) isn't *Wishing Well*, so *High Life*. Louise wrote *Wishing Well*.
Thus:
Cindy Ross - *High Life* - 4 stars;
Clive Kent - *Danger Money* - 2 stars;
Geoff Bowler - *Milestone* - 3 stars;
Louise Jameson - *Wishing Well* - 1 star;
Margot Price - *Heaven Sent* - 5 stars.

70

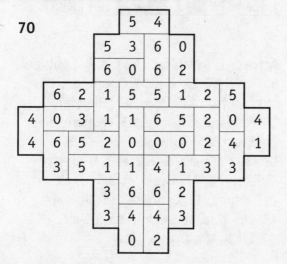

71

2	6	3	1	4	5
9	5	7	8	6	4
3	4	5	6	7	8
7	3	2	8	9	1
9	2	1	7	8	9
4	1	3	5	6	2

SOLUTIONS

72

Across: 1. Rhyme, 4. Ladle, 7. Degenerated, 8. Eli, 9. Steeple, 11. Natural, 14. Cad, 16. Downhearted, 17. Sauna, 18. Frame.

Down: 1. Redie, 2. Ylgnittiwnu, 3. Egnis, 4. Lorne, 5. Detapicitna, 6. Eudne, 10. Tna, 11. Nades, 12. Rohba, 13. Liarf, 15. Dedne.

73

1. Trapezium, 2. Mortar, 3. Reticence, 4. Eagle, 5. Eclair, 6. Regicide, 7. Eleven, 8. Normality, 9. Yashmak, 10. Klaxon, 11. Numerous, 12. Snorkel, 13. Labyrinth, 14. Habitation, 15. Newcomer, 16. Righteous, 17. Samurai, 18. Illusion, 19. Navigator, 20. Rubella, 21. Aluminium, 22. Madeira, 23. Anarchist, 24. Testimony, 25. Yankee.

Hidden name: INGMAR BERGMAN

74

```
P  A R R E K O O L       L
R  N                     N
O  D     A C I D         O
L  U     L       A       O
O  N     I       R       P
G  C     G       E       M
U  E     H T     T       A
E  N             S       L
L  S U R E G I           U
I                        F
T  E N A C I O U S E
```

75

```
. . . . B . . D I A N E
T . W E N D Y . . N . M
A . H . L . O . . N . M
N . I . I . R O S I E . A
Y O L A N D E . . N . . S
A . A . D . E . . G . . Y
. A R I A D N E . R U B Y
. . Y . . E . L . I . . L
. D . E R I C A . D . . V
L E E . . R . I . . G . I
. L . . A . D . N . V E R A
. L . M U R I E L . R .
M A R Y . E . . . . T I N A
```

76

```
G I E E R C N I E K
A R R D O C G U Y N
F F L F D O N E B O
H E I L I L R P I M
I P Z O W E E H S L
O P A R X L N T O E
P E L D N Y A P N M
O S E P A R D N C A
T U P O E L T O I L
A M H A N T I G E R
```

77

Across: 1. Default, 5. Award, 8. Cobbler, 9. Prays, 10. Scene, 11. Opening, 12. Clouts, 14. Surges, 17. Blender, 19. Rapid, 22. Awake, 23. Hygiene, 24. Erect, 25. Rotated.

Down: 1. Docks, 2. Fable, 3. Ugliest, 4. Terror, 5. Ample, 6. Amazing, 7. Designs, 12. Cabbage, 13. Operate, 15. Upright, 16. Arthur, 18. Dwelt, 20. Pleat, 21. Dread.

SOLUTIONS

78

Film in shaded
column:
Memphis Belle

M	O	R	E	L	L	O
E	N	D	O	R	S	E
M	I	S	T	A	K	E
P	R	O	P	H	E	T
H	A	M	M	O	C	K
I	M	P	I	O	U	S
S	U	P	R	E	M	E
B	R	I	G	A	D	E
E	R	E	C	T	E	D
L	A	M	B	A	D	A
L	O	B	B	I	E	S
E	P	I	C	U	R	E

79

		W	O	O	
T	R	A	I	N	
E	A	G	L	E	
E	Y	E			

		B	A	T	
T	O	R	C	H	
O	R	A	T	E	
N	E	T			

80

DE	AR	TH		TR	AD	ES		PR	IN	CE
TA		AW	AK	EN		KI	SM	ET		YL
IN	DE	ED		DY	NA	MO		TY	CO	ON
	ME				RR				HE	
BL	AN	CH		DR	OW	SY		UN	RE	AL
ON		AN	OR	AK		ST	AS	IS		BE
DE	LU	GE		ES	TE	EM		EX	PE	RT
	ST				DI				NC	
SE	RE	NE		AC	UM	EN		SO	IL	ED
VE		ST	AN	CE		CA	RR	OT		IB
RE	VI	LE		DE	PO	SE		HE	CK	LE

81

An apple is 17p, a pear 18p, a
banana 22p and a pineapple 50p.
A carrot is 11p, an onion is 28p, a
leek is 31p and a cabbage 69p.

82

Starting top left: 1. Trap, 2. Mitre,
3. Vale, 4. Pallet, 5. Race, 6. Dolt,
7. Lewd.
Starting bottom left: 1. Dwelt,
2. Lode, 3. Cartel, 4. Lapel, 5. Avert,
6. Impart.

83

6F contains no symbol from column F.

84

SOLUTIONS

85

	Y		A		S		M		M		A	
N	1	L	2	P	3	E	4	A	5	B	6	E
	X		C		Y		T		E		L	
E	7	I	8	A	9	S	10	J	11	R	12	A
	T		D		T		E		K		E	
C	13	E	14	F	15	L	16	I	17	S	18	V
	H		A		E		D		D		A	
A	19	M	20	F	21	A	22	P	23	O	24	X
	R		E		T		M		R		C	
E	25	P	26	W	27	R	28	Y	29	U	30	T
	I		T		A		A		B		D	
V	31	E	32	N	33	W	34	L	35	M	36	R
	W		A		D		F		A		U	

86

Thoughtlessness

87

1. c, 2. b, 3. a, 4. a, 5. b, 6. c,
7. c, 8. a, 9. b, 10. c, 11. b,
12. a, 13. c, 14. b, 15. a.

88

Implant, Pliant, Paint, Pint, Point,
Potion, Portion

89

The hidden word is TOPSOIL

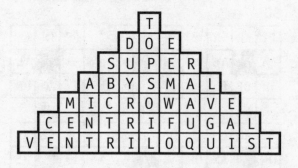

90

		D		O		L		A
A	H	E	A	D		U	R	N
	A	C	I	D		N		G
A	R	K	S		S	A	L	E
	S		L	A	U	R	E	L
S	H	O	E		M		E	
		A		V		A	R	T
P	A	R	T	I	E	D		I
	T		H	E	R	O	I	C
H	O	S	E		A		N	
	N	U	M	B		B	E	T
H	E	R		A	D	O	R	E
	D	E	N	Y		A	T	E

91

1. Beaker, 2. Kettle, 3. Tunnel,
4. Warren, 5. Narrow, 6. Branch.

92

6	x	2	−	8	+	3	=	7
−		x		+		x		
3	+	6	−	2	x	8	=	56
x		−		x		−		
8	−	3	x	6	+	2	=	32
+		+		−		+		
2	x	8	+	3	−	6	=	13
=		=		=		=		
26		17		57		28		

SOLUTIONS

93

11	+	13	x	12	−	14	=	274
x		+		+		−		
14	−	12	x	13	+	11	=	37
−		x		x		+		
12	−	11	x	14	+	13	=	27
+		−		−		x		
13	+	14	−	11	x	12	=	192
=		=		=		=		
155		261		339		192		

94

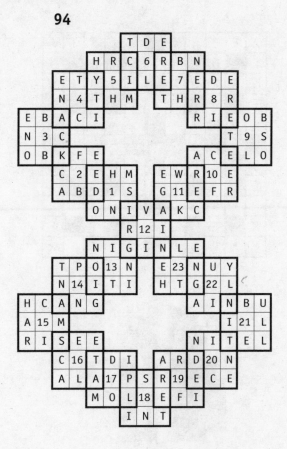

						T	D	E						
				H	R	C	6	R	B	N				
		E	T	Y	5	I	L	E	7	E	D	E		
		N	4	T	H	M		T	H	R	8	R		
E	B	A	C	I						R	I	E	O	B
N	3	C										T	9	S
O	B	K	F	E						A	C	E	L	O
		C	2	E	H	M		E	W	R	10	E		
		A	B	D	1	S		G	11	E	F	R		
				O	N	I	V	A	K	C				
						R	12	I						
				N	I	G	I	N	L	E				
		T	P	O	13	N		E	23	N	U	Y		
		N	14	I	T	I		H	T	G	22	L		
H	C	A	N	G						A	I	N	B	U
A	15	M										I	21	L
R	I	S	E	E						N	I	T	E	L
		C	16	T	D	I		A	R	D	20	N		
		A	L	A	17	P	S	R	19	E	C	E		
				M	O	L	18	E	F	I				
						I	N	T						

95

A	I	N					S	U	P	E	R	I	O	R
R			C	A	M		O		I				R	
A	R	N	O				U		T	I	G	R	I	S
L			M		L		T						N	
S	E	A	O	F	O	K	H	O	T	S	K		O	
E		N			I		C						C	
A		T			R		H		Y	E	L	L	O	W
	L	A	K	E	E	R	I	E				O		
A		R					N		T	H	A	M	E	S
V	I	C	T	O	R	I	A					O		E
O		T		X			S	E	V	E	R	N		A
N		I		U			E					D		O
		C	A	S	P	I	A	N	S	E	A			F
		O				T		I		X		T		J
P	A	C	I	F	I	C		L		E		W		A
		E				H		E				E		P
B	L	A	C	K	S	E	A		G	E	N	E	V	A
		N				N						D		N

96

1. Willpower, 2. Worldwide,
3. Treachery, 4. Harmonica,
5. Identical, 6. Ignoramus,
7. Imaginary, 8. Justified,
9. Kangaroos.

97

Z	E	B	R	A		V	I	S	T	A
E		U		N	E	E		A		X
S	A	X	O	N		E	Q	U	A	L
T		O		O	A	R		D		E
Y	U	M	M	Y		S	N	I	P	S
	S		A				E		E	
J	E	E	P	S		C	O	U	G	H
E		A		A	W	E		N		I
R	E	G	A	L		D	E	F	E	R
K		E		E	K	E		I		E
Y	A	R	D	S		D	E	T	E	R

98

E - B is an upside down reflection of A; and E is an upside down reflection of C.

99

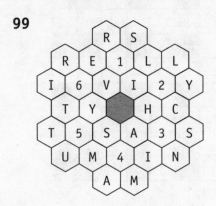

100

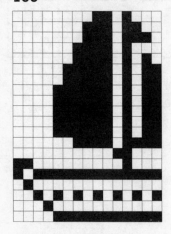

101

Fourteen.

102

Suki lives at No 8 but not with the Masons (clue 2), Mortons (clue 1) or Monroes (3), so the McDonalds. Whisky lives at either No 4 or No 6 (1), as does Lucky (4), so Toots lives at No 2. Lucky lives at No 6 and the ginger cat at No 4 (4). By elimination, Whisky is at No 4. Toots is black and belongs to the Mortons (1). The Masons don't own Lucky (4), so Whisky. The Monroes own Lucky. Suki is white (3), so Lucky is tabby.
Thus:
Mason family - No 4 - Whisky - ginger;
McDonald family - No 8 - Suki - white;
Monroe family - No 6 - Lucky - tabby;
Morton family - No 2 - Toots - black.

103

HIDE-bide-bids-beds-bees-
   sees-SEEK;
FLESH-flash-flask-blank-blank-
   bland-blond-BLOOD;
BREAD-break-bleak-bleat-blest-
   blast-boast-TOAST.

SOLUTIONS

104

```
2 9 1 4 3 5 8 7 6
6 8 7 2 1 9 5 4 3
3 4 5 6 8 7 2 1 9
9 1 6 8 4 3 7 5 2
4 3 8 5 7 2 6 9 1
5 7 2 9 6 1 3 8 4
8 2 9 1 5 6 4 3 7
1 5 3 7 2 4 9 6 8
7 6 4 3 9 8 1 2 5
```

105

P	L	A	C	E
L	E	M	O	N
A	M	E	N	D
C	O	N	G	O
E	N	D	O	W

106

1. Top Cat, 2. Batman, 3. Thunderbirds, 4. Fireman Sam, 5. Teletubbies, 6. The Flintstones, 7. Digimon, 8. Rugrats, 9. Tweenies, 10. Dangermouse.

107

Across: 1. Factory, 5. Cobra, 8. Tabasco, 9. Moose, 10. Later, 11. Against, 12. Diesel, 14. Attend, 17. Atheist, 19. Uncut, 22. Excel, 23. Retsina, 24. Tally, 25. Haddock.

Down: 1. Fatal, 2. Cabot, 3. Observe, 4. Yeoman, 5. Comma, 6. Brownie, 7. Alerted, 12. Dearest, 13. Ethical, 15. Taunted, 16. Starch, 18. Inlay, 20. Cairo, 21. Thank.

108

109

110

Here are just a few of the words you could have made: Agent, And, Anger, Danger, Darn, Dean, Dent, Earn, End, Gander, Garden, Gnat, Grand, Grant, Granted, Nag, Near, Neat, Net, Ran, Rand, Rang, Range, Ranged, Rant, Ranted, Rent, Tan, Tang, Tarn, Ten, Tend, Tern, Trend.

111

112

Cards total 78 (intro), so the king is missing. Card E is a heart (clue 4), so G is a diamond (intro) and F and H are spades or clubs, as are A, C, I and K (intro). Since there is no king, H isn't the jack (4). Thus the jack is F, the 2 of hearts is J and the 7 is I. D is a heart, so B and L are diamonds (intro). H is the 9 (4). The ace is C (2), the 5 is B and the 4 is G. The queen (3) is A and the 8 is E. A and K are clubs (3) and C and I are spades. K is the 10 (4), so (5) H is a spade and F is a club. The 6 isn't a heart (5), so is L is the 6 and D is the 3. Thus:

QC 5D AS 3H
8H JC 4D 9S
7S 2H 10C 6D

114

1. Stockist, 2. Tailored, 3. Debut,
4. Teacher, 5. Rice, 6. Evil, 7. Lance,
8. Easier, 9. Repast, 10. Talent,
11. Trendy, 12. Yoghurt, 13. Trot.
Transport: Bicycle

113

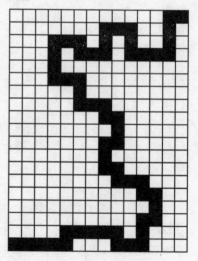

116

The hidden word is:
PESETA.

S	P	A	T	U	L	A		U
Y		L		N		U	R	N
C	A	L	M	E	S	T		Q
O		E		A		H		U
P	E	R	I	S	C	O	P	E
H		G		I		R		E
A		I	B	E	R	I	A	N
N	E	E		S		S		L
T		S	A	T	I	E	T	Y

115

1. Adult, 2. Tomorrow,
3. Wash, 4. Hoe,
5. Exactly, 6. Yell,
7. Love, 8. Extra.

117

```
H O M E L E S S ▓ C A R P E T
E   E   O   T ▓ B   B   A   I
A L L O Y ▓ R E A S S U R E D
R   O   A   N ▓ ▓ O   T   I
S I D E L I N E D ▓ R A Y O N
E   R   ▓ G   I ▓ B       E
▓ D A Z Z L E ▓ T H E R M O S
V   M   I       ▓ N   A   S
A N A G R A M ▓ S A T I R E ▓
S   ▓ C   E   U ▓ ▓ G     D
C A M E O ▓ D I S S I P A T E
U   U   N   I ▓ P   S   R   N
L A S S I T U D E ▓ S A I N T
A   I   U   M ▓ C   U   N   A
R A C E M E ▓ E T H E R E A L
```

118

1. a, 2. d, 3. c, 4. d, 5. c, 6. b, 7. a, 8. a, 9. d, 10. c, 11. a, 12. b.

119

Across: 4. Boo, 6. Agony, 9. Specimen, 10. Possess, 14. Garage, 15. Gremlin, 16. Need, 17. Sleeting, 20. Megalith, 22. Essay, 25. Alibi, 27. Waste, 30. Chairman, 31. Ancestry, 34. Puss, 35. Channel, 36. Thwart, 37. Aerated, 39. Orphaned, 40. Abide, 41. Egg.

Down: 1. Abyss, 2. Moderate, 3. Zone, 5. Origami, 7. Revenge, 8. Tolerant, 11. Salvia, 12. Sunshade, 13. Guess, 18. Evict, 19. Tricycle, 21. Era, 23. Stranger, 24. Aga, 26. Banana, 28. Sauce, 29. Eastern, 32. Cowshed, 33. Shrunken, 37. Adage, 38. Raid.

120

```
H   U R E H S U O U
O   P               C
S   T   P A E H   C O
T   O   P       C O N
I   R   A       O P N
L   N   R       P E I
E   A   E L     E   S
G   D           C   S
I   O M I N A N     A
S                   S
L A T E Q U I L A S
```

121

```
  R   N   W   V   R   L
E 1 O 2 E 3 A 4 I 5 O 6 A
S   P   D   D   N   V
P 7 N 8 A 9 P 10 R 11 E 12 O
A   I   M   O   A   L
S 13 C 14 N 15 O 16 B 17 E 18 S
K   O   A   T   L   E
G 19 I 20 N 21 O 22 S 23 I 24 D
N   L   L   P   A   L
I 25 G 26 O 27 E 28 T 29 M 30 I
W   N   S   R   E   A
I 31 T 32 E 33 A 34 E 35 P 36 C
N   S   V   G   L   T
```

122

Starting top left: 1. Peel, 2. Salami, 3. Natal, 4. Fetish, 5. Cable, 6. Grime.
Starting bottom left: 1. Emir, 2. Gel, 3. Bach, 4. Site, 5. Flat, 6. Animal, 7. Asleep.

SOLUTIONS

123

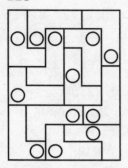

125

By elimination, squares 11 and 17 (clue 1) both contain an R, so (clue 2) squares 4 and 19 both contain an X. In line 1-49, the X isn't in square 9 (4), so 41. Since squares 13 and 38 (3) contain (by elimination) either I or E and since (by elimination) square 10 contains either I or E, then 24=U and (4) squares 5 and 9 contain T. In row 1-7, the R is in either 2 or 7, so there's no R in 37. Nor (in row 36-42) is there an R in 42 (1) or 36 (5), so there's an R in 40. Thus (6) the R in line 7-43 is in 43 and (above) 2=R. In 1-49, the U is in either 1 or 49, so 7=I, 13=E, 10=I, 38=E (3), 6=U, 1=E, 49=U, 25=M, 37=U, 33=I, 16=M, 20=T, 18=U, 26=E, 47=M, 34=M, 48=I, 32=E, 44=E, 30=X, 23=I, 35=R, 29=U, 46=T and 39=I. The X in row 8-14 is in 14 (2), so 8=M, 36=T, 22=X, 28=T and 42=M.

Thus:

```
E  R  M  X  T  U  I
M  T  I  R  U  E  X
I  M  R  U  X  T  E
X  I  U  M  E  R  T
U  X  T  E  I  M  R
T  U  E  I  R  X  M
R  E  X  T  M  I  U
```

124

John's find was in the High Street, Gwen's in Tender Terrace and Ross's in Bank Street. Sean's wasn't in Stash Lane, so Money Mews. Trudy's was in Stash Lane. Gwen found either 1p or 2p. If 2p, then Sean found 10p. But then Trudy can't have found twice as much as Ross. So Gwen found 1p and Sean 5p. Trudy found 20p and Ross 10p. John found 2p. Thus:

Gwen - 1p - Tender Terrace;
Ross - 10p - Bank Street;
Sean - 5p - Money Mews;
Trudy - 20p - Stash Lane.

126

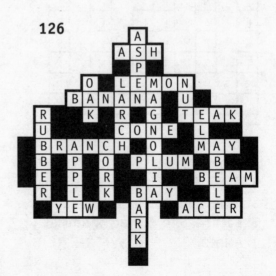

SOLUTIONS

127

2	6	3	1	4	5
9	5	7	8	6	4
3	4	5	6	7	8
7	3	2	8	9	1
9	2	1	7	8	9
4	1	3	5	6	2

128

	F		A		A		D	
P	R	O	T	E	C	T	O	R
	U		O	F	T		N	
A	G	E	N	T		S	K	I
	A		E	S	T	E	E	M
A	L	L			E	N	Y	A
		A	S	S	E	T		M
E	S	P	I	E	D		T	
	H	E	R	A		C	O	G
P	A	L		L		O	R	E
	L		F		O	M	E	N
P	L	I	A	B	L	E		O
	O	R	B		E	T	N	A
D	W	E	L	T			U	
	E		E	R	E	C	T	S
A	R	K		O		A	S	H
		O	A	T		L		E
H	E	A	L		P	I	L	E
	A	L	E		S	C	O	T
F	R	A	C	T	I	O	U	S

129

1. Robust, 2. Ornate,
3. Petrol, 4. Planet,
5. Melted, 6. Double.

130

Across: 1. Smooth,
4. Tariff, 8. Meant,
10. Panda, 11. Larch,
12. Lease, 14. Agree,
16. Par, 18. Axle,
19. Adam, 21. Gin,
24. Bathe, 27. Serum,
29. Adorn, 30. Eager,
31. Anger, 32. Tetchy,
33. Beetle.
Down: 1. Simple,
2. Omaha, 3. Title,
5. Alpha, 6. Inner,
7. Frayed, 9. Area,
13. Sixth, 15. Grave,
16. Peg, 17. Ran,
20. Object, 22. Iron,
23. Emerge, 25. Tight,
26. Earth, 27. Snake,
28. Right.

131

P	L	O	T		D		E		C	
L		B		G	R	U	M	B	L	E
E		E		A		I		I		
A	S	Y	L	U	M		G	L	E	E
S		A		A		R		N		
E	N	T	R	Y		F	A	I	T	H
	E		G		A		T		E	
F	A	K	E		C	L	E	V	E	R
	R		S		U		I		M	
O	B	E	S	I	T	Y		L		I
	Y		E		E		H	E	A	T

132

Only one of either the triangle, spade,
diamond and star ISN'T in the solution (2),
so neither the heart nor the circle is in (4),
nor is the square (3). Thus the club is in the
4th position (1). The star is in 1st position
(4), thus the triangle isn't in the solution.
So the spade and diamond are both in the
solution (2). The spade isn't in 2nd position
(2), so 3rd. The diamond is in 2nd position.
Thus: ☆ ◆ ♠ ♣

133

The missing letter is F - and its value is 11.

J	B	V	S		T	Q	A	H
U	K	E	L	E	L	E		E	Q	U	A	B	L	Y
G	A	I	C		X	A	R	P
G	I	G	G	L	E	R		T	H	R	O	U	G	H
L		L		E		I	R	P	E
E	L	E	M	E	N	T	A	L		E	A	T	E	N
		M		E		L	L	E
A	C	R	O	B	A	T		S	P	L	A	Y	E	D
R		E		R		E		E
A	U	D	I	O		A	Q	U	E	D	U	C	T	S
B		E		I	B		P		O	E
I	N	S	I	D	E	R		W	I	Z	E	N	E	D
A			I	E	E		A	E	V	D
N	I	G	E	R	I	A		R	E	S	P	E	C	T
S		N		Y	K	D		T	X	E

134

1. MarGin, 2. WaLlet, 3. RepAir,
4. LoNdon, 5. CanCer, 6. FrEeze.
Thus – GLANCE.

135

MA	DD	EN		UN	EA	SE		AR	MA	DA
DR		CO	AR	SE		CU	RA	RE		WD
AS	HO	RE		EN	DU	RE		ST	AB	LE
	LL				ST				OU	
EM	ER	GE		SH	ER	PA		HI	ND	ER
PI		NI	CK	EL		UP	BE	AT		AS
RE	VE	AL		VE	NE	ER		US	UR	ER
	LC				CT				GE	
MO	RO	SE		CH	AR	GE		DE	NT	AL
BI		CO	FF	EE		NI	MB	LE		LU
LE	GE	ND		SE	AM	US		TE	NU	RE

136

A	B	C	A	C	B
C	C	B	B	A	A
B	A	A	B	C	C
B	B	C	C	A	A
A	A	B	C	B	C
C	C	A	A	B	B

137

Ray's stage name was Viper and the bass player's was Cobra (clue 1), so the drummer whose real name had the same initial as his stage name (clue 3) was (by elimination) Rattler, alias Rick. The lead guitarist was either Colin or Chris (5) and Dave was known as Python. By elimination, Boa was the lead guitarist. Dave wasn't the keyboard player (2), so lead singer. The keyboard player was Ray. Chris was Boa (4), so Colin was Cobra. Thus:

Chris - Boa - lead guitar;
Colin - Cobra - bass guitar;
Dave - Python - lead singer;
Ray - Viper - keyboard;
Rick - Rattler - drums.

SOLUTIONS

138

5	1	6	5	4	0	3
3	0	2	3	4	5	4
2	6	2	3	1	6	3
4	4	5	1	6	1	6
5	0	4	2	6	1	0
2	3	5	0	0	3	2
6	4	5	4	1	2	1
0	5	3	1	6	0	2

140

Here are just a few of the words you could have made: Able, Abler, Ale, Ape, Arable, Are, Bale, Bare, Bear, Blear, Blare, Brae, Ear, Earl, Era, Lea, Leap, Pale, Parable, Pare, Pea, Peal, Pear, Pearl, Plea, Rape, Rea, Real, Reap, Rep.

142

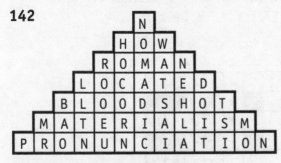

The hidden word is: NOMADIC.

144

1. Alternatively, 2. Youngster, 3. Reconciliation, 4. Naughtiness, 5. Steeplechaser, 6. Realising, 7. Gastronomic, 8. Ceremoniously, 9. Yearning, 10. Gestation, 11. Nevertheless, 12. Somersaulting, 13. Gardener, 14. Restitution, 15. Nearsighted, 16. Decentralisation, 17. Neutral, 18. Leicestershire, 19. Experienced, 20. Disliking, 21. Gossip, 22. Promenade, 23. Earthquake.

139

O	R	E		H	O	S	T		U	R	D	U
D	A	Y		E	M	I	R		P	E	A	S
E	T	E	R	N	I	T	Y		S	I	R	E
			A	C	T			D	E	T	E	R
P	E	A	C	E		T	R	I	T	E		
L	A	C	E		T	R	E	E		R	O	W
E	R	A		W	H	E	A	T		A	P	E
A	N	D		H	A	N	D		S	T	E	P
	E	M	E	N	D		S	C	E	N	T	
A	D	M	I	T		B	O	A				
T	O	I	L		F	L	O	U	R	I	S	H
O	N	C	E		L	E	A	N		C	H	A
M	E	S	S		Y	A	R	D		Y	E	T

141

L	A	T	E	R
A	B	O	V	E
T	O	T	A	L
E	V	A	D	E
R	E	L	E	T

E	M	B	E	D
M	O	L	A	R
B	L	A	R	E
E	A	R	N	S
D	R	E	S	S

143

1. Truss, 2. September, 3. Berserk, 4. Knife, 5. Feeler, 6. Erosion, 7. Onset.

SOLUTIONS

145

W	E	I	R	D	L	Y
H	O	N	E	S	T	Y
O	V	A	T	I	O	N
D	E	N	T	I	S	T
A	D	O	P	T	E	D
R	E	D	R	E	S	S
E	R	O	S	I	O	N
S	P	A	R	T	A	N
W	A	L	L	A	B	Y
I	R	E	L	A	N	D
N	U	M	B	E	R	S
S	C	A	M	P	E	R

Motto: WHO DARES WINS

146

9	5	9	7	3	1
7	8	5	6	9	3
2	4	6	5	3	1
7	6	8	4	6	2
2	1	7	3	5	4
4	8	9	2	1	8

147

B	O	U	R	B	O	N	
T	E	Q	U	I	L	A	
C	A	M	P	A	R	I	
A	M	O	R	O	S	O	
C	H	I	A	N	T	I	
M	A	R	T	I	N	I	
W	H	I	S	K	E	Y	
S	A	M	B	U	C	A	

148

1. Friday, 2. Fatter, 3. Tea-set, 4. Saline, 5. Driven, 6. Divide.

149

Across: 1. Brook, 4. Gavel, 7. Octopus, 8. Lop, 9. Rationale, 13. Condiment, 19. Mar, 20. Private, 21. Ideal, 22. Trend.

Down: 1. Boot, 2. Otter, 3. Kaput, 4. Gusto, 5. Villa, 6. Lapsed, 10. Aid, 11. Nun, 12. Scampi, 14. Nurse, 15. Impel, 16. Edict, 17. Trade, 18. Deed.

150

7	−	5	×	3	+	9	=	15
×		+		+		−		
3	×	9	+	7	−	5	=	29
−		−		−		×		
9	+	3	−	5	×	7	=	49
+		×		×		+		
5	×	7	+	9	−	3	=	41
=		=		=		=		
17		77		45		31		

151

7	+	2	−	4	×	6	=	30
×		+		×		−		
4	×	6	−	7	+	2	=	19
+		−		+		+		
2	×	4	−	6	+	7	=	9
−		×		−		×		
6	+	7	×	2	−	4	=	22
=		=		=		=		
24		28		32		44		

SOLUTIONS

152

Across: 1. Picnic, 4. Falter, 8. Reich, 9. Aborted, 10. Under, 11. Chalice, 12. Ill, 13. Evict, 14. Aniseed, 15. Theorem, 17. Nasal, 20. Unfit, 21. Denizen, 22. Stratum, 24. Light, 25. David, 28. Naughty, 31. Dynasty, 32. Cured, 34. Lie, 35. Shamble, 36. Roost, 37. Animals, 38. Alien, 39. Remedy, 40. Enrage.

Down: 1. Perjure, 2. Childlike, 3. Inheritor, 5. Adoration, 6. Tattiness, 7. Redhead, 9. Acclaimed, 15. Trussed, 16. Origami, 18. Abiding, 19. Lengthy, 23. Moneyless, 26. Vandalism, 27. Dashboard, 29. Uncertain, 30. Harmonica, 31. Despair, 33. Detente.

153

Starting top left: 1. Trade, 2. Matter, 3. Felt, 4. Tender, 5. Beta, 6. Ballet.
Starting bottom left: 1. Tell, 2. Abate, 3. Bred, 4. Nettle, 5. Fret, 6. Tamed, 7. Art.

154

		F		S		
	T	R	O	P	H	Y
	E		O			E
	B	E	A	T	E	N
			D		Y	
	E	L	O	P	E	D
		A	L	E		E

	D		D		S	V	E	L	T	E
M	A	N	I	A		A	S	T	I	R
	T		V	I	A		C		L	
F	A	T	A	L		T	E	S	T	S
		E		M	E	A	N	T		A
A	G	A	P	E			S	T	A	R	T
		A		U	N	I	T		R	U	E
S	L	E	P	T		E	M	E	N	D

155

1. Pasture, 2. Expect, 3. Tactics, 4. Sharp, 5. Prawn, 6. Needs, 7. Stop.

156

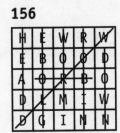

157

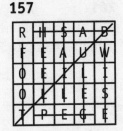

158

1. Tom ThumB, 2. BavariA, 3. ActinG, 4. BlusH, 5. AchE, 6. BeE, 7. OR, 8. A. The character is thus: BAGHEERA.

SOLUTIONS

159

The yellow hat is immediately next to and right of the green hat (clue 1). The red hat is more than one place left of the white hat (clue 4). Thus C is yellow, B is green, A is red and D is white. Neither B nor C was bought in March (6), so (3) D was bought in March and (6) B in January. D has a purple ribbon (5) and (2) C a black ribbon. B has a blue ribbon (3) and A was bought in July and has a pink ribbon. C was bought in May.

Thus:

A - red hat - pink ribbon - July;

B - green hat - blue ribbon - January;

C - yellow hat - black ribbon - May;

D - white hat - purple ribbon - March.

160

Across: 1. Helping hand, 7. Ink, 9. Baize, 10. Unrelated, 11. Tidal wave, 12. Gorge, 13. Annoyed, 16. Enter, 17. Urn, 19. Robin, 21. Theatre, 24. Alive, 25. Avalanche, 28. Insistent, 29. Toils, 30. Gas, 31. Disgraceful.

Down: 1. Habitual, 2. Laird, 3. Ideally, 4. Gouda, 5. Agreement, 6. Delight, 7. Interpret, 8. Kidney, 14. Narcissus, 15. Dungarees, 18. Reversal, 20. Blessed, 22. Elastic, 23. Having, 26. Altar, 27. Chief.

161

A - The three figures in each vertical column add up to 39, 40 and 41 respectively.

163

Wine

1	2	3
Fr white	Eng red	G rosé
4	**5**	**6**
G red	Fr rosé	Eng white
7	**8**	**9**
Eng rosé	G white	Fr red

and

162

A	E	D	U	S	A	R	C
P	M	S	E	A	N	S	I
H	R	O	L	L	I	S	U
H	S	D	I	C	H	A	S
A	U	R	T	A	N	T	L
D	E	A	E	J	O	S	A
P	S	C	I	A	S	P	A
R	E	T	A	R	O	D	N
O	M	H	E	A	R	M	I
S	I	S	U	S	T	E	S
H	E	E	M	E	E	R	A
C	R	S	D	N	S	S	U
U	L	E	I	O	N	Y	S

Dine

The first 120 miles at 40mph took three hours. The remaining 120 miles at 80mph took ninety minutes (or one and a half hours). Thus Fred was half an hour late.

SOLUTIONS

164

Cards total 80 (intro), so the jack is missing. Card E has a value two lower than I (clue 3), so E isn't the king or 9 (intro). K isn't the 3 (clue 2), so G isn't the 4 (4). If K is the 4, then F is the 9 (1) and G is the 5 (4), leaving nowhere to fit the cards in clue 2. The 9 is above the king (1), so isn't G (4), thus (1) the 9 is C, the king of spades is G and H is the 4. E is a club (intro) and F and H are either hearts or diamonds. B, J, D and L are either spades or clubs; so (2) the 10 of diamonds is F, B is the 3 and E is the 6. H is a heart (intro). I is the 8 (3). K is the queen (4) which is either a heart or diamond (intro), so (5) is a diamond, as is the ace. Cards C and I are hearts (intro), so the ace is A. B is a club (5), as is L. D and J are spades. The 7 is L (5). D is the 2 (4) and J is the 5.

Thus:

AD 3C 9H 2S
6C 10D KS 4H
8H 5S QD 7C

166

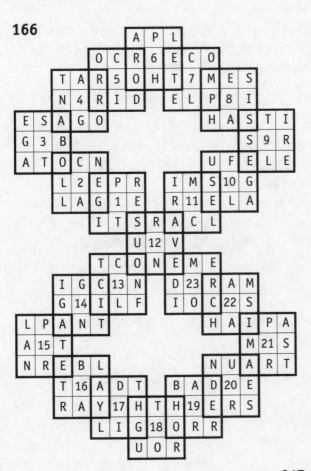

165

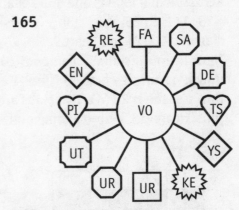

167

(grid puzzle)

168

Circumnavigated.

SOLUTIONS

169

1. Pancreas, 2. Sangria, 3. Atavism, 4. Malaria, 5. Alexander, 6. Republic, 7. Camelot, 8. Toby jug, 9. Gazelle, 10. Einstein, 11. Nepal, 12. Lower-case, 13. Esperanto, 14. Octagon, 15. Neutron, 16. Nougat, 17. Tiger lily, 18. Yale, 19. Ethelred.
Hidden name: EVELYN WAUGH

170

GIN-din-die-dye-aye-ALE, DEAD-head-herd-here-hire-hive-LIVE, INK-inn-ion-don-den-PEN, WATER-pater-payer-pryer-fryer-freer-freed-breed-bread-broad-brood-BLOOD.

171

Across: A diamond is one more than a heart (lines 1 and 2), so (4) a club + 2 diamonds = 23+1+1, so 25. Thus club + heart + diamond = 24, so (1) a spade is 7. A club is 5 (3), diamond 10 (2) and heart 9.
Thus: heart=9, club=5, diamond=10 and spade=7.

Down: A heart is worth 15 (lines 1 and 4), so (line 3) a club and a diamond total 40. Thus a spade is 20 (4). Two clubs are 44 (2), so a club is 22 and (1) a diamond is 18.
Thus: heart=15, club=22, diamond=18 and spade=20.

172

9	−	2	x	4	+	7	=	35
−		+		x		−		
7	−	4	+	9	x	2	=	24
+		x		+		x		
4	x	7	+	2	−	9	=	21
x		−		−		+		
2	+	9	−	7	x	4	=	16
=		=		=		=		
12		33		31		49		

173

Across: 1. Nasal, 4. Manor, 7. Emu, 8. Reeve, 9. Mug, 10. Haste, 13. Sec, 15. Else, 17. Alien, 18. Tame, 20. Icy, 22. Stock, 25. Era, 26. Excel, 27. Sir, 28. Gecko, 29. Tacit.

Down: 1. Neris, 2. Ssehc, 3. Leeh, 4. Muls, 5. Nomel, 6. Regae, 11. Anihc, 12. Ten, 14. Ela, 16. Soc, 17. Aet, 18. Taerg, 19. Msahc, 20. Itcac, 21. Yllat, 23. Olso, 24. Kert.

174

1. Sextet, 2. Tablet, 3. Bilbao, 4. Nibble, 5. Nectar, 6. Strain.

175

Across: 1. Thankless, 7. Liege, 8. Dwell, 9. Nightingale, 11. Incompetent, 13. Adorn, 14. Ibsen, 16. Slaughter.

Down: 1. Talon, 2. Ate, 3. Kleptomania, 4. Endangering, 5. Seepage, 6. False, 10. Geckoes, 11. Irate, 12. Tenor, 15. Sot.

SOLUTIONS

176

Across: 9. Goading, 10. Acetate, 11. Abdomen, 12. Sceptre, 13. Astronaut, 15. Seeds, 16. Breathe, 19. Orbital, 20. Mafia, 21. Barbecued, 25. Ancient, 26. Sustain, 28. Execute, 29. Devalue.

Down: 1. Iguana, 2. Bandit, 3. Firm, 4. Agenda, 5. Falsetto, 6. Defensible, 7. Tastiest, 8. Reversal, 14. Outrageous, 16. Bemoaned, 17. Effected, 18. Embitter, 22. Reside, 23. Unable, 24. Denier, 27. Save.

177

S	C	A	R	F		B	R	A		S	E	A
C	O	R	A	L		R	A	G		T	A	N
U	N	I	T	Y		A	N	A	L	Y	S	T
D	E	L	I		E	G	G		Y	E	T	I
		O	F	T		E	A	R				
S	P	A		O	N	E		L	E	A	P	T
A	R	M		R	A	B	B	I		L	E	O
T	O	P	I	C		B	O	B		P	R	Y
			T	E	D		R	I	M			
D	O	M	E		A	T	E		A	M	O	N
A	N	E	M	O	N	E		E	R	A	T	O
I	C	E		A	C	E		A	C	R	I	D
S	E	T		F	E	N		T	H	E	S	E

178

Across: 1. Shell, 5. Threw, 8. Ounce, 9. Opt, 10. Robot, 11. Spasm, 14. Dart, 17. Tear, 19. Allergy, 20. Aims, 21. Pail, 22. Termite, 23. Rely, 24. Step, 27. Impel, 30. Attic, 32. Use, 33. Elver, 34. Heard, 35. Debut.

Down: 1. Scold, 2. Enter, 3. Loss, 4. Inca, 5. Term, 6. Rib, 7. Water, 12. Pilgrim, 13. Sardine, 15. Alike, 16. Tasty, 17. Types, 18. Arise, 23. Reach, 25. Thumb, 26. Pleat, 27. Iced, 28. Pave, 29. Lard, 31. Tea.

179

Starting top left: 1. Elapse, 2. Dahlia, 3. Vats, 4. Rifle, 5. Errata, 6. Mall.
Starting bottom left: 1. Llama, 2. Tar, 3. Reel, 4. First, 5. Avail, 6. Hades, 7. Pale.

181

Ablaze, Adverb, Fulfil, Larynx, Luxury, Minnow, Poison, Possum, Pronto, Squirt, Thirty, Trophy, Typhus, Upshot, Vortex, Wintry.

180

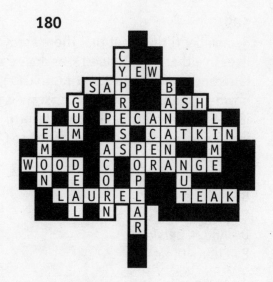

SOLUTIONS

182

Doorman, Random, Adorn, Rand, Nadir, Inroad, Adoring.

183

1. a, 2. c, 3. c, 4. a, 5. b, 6. b, 7. a, 8. b, 9. a, 10. b, 11. c, 12. a, 13. a, 14. b, 15. c.

184

A	B	C	C	A	B
B	C	A	B	C	A
C	A	A	B	B	C
B	B	C	C	A	A
C	A	B	A	B	C
A	C	B	A	C	B

185

186

E	N	D
N	E	E
D	E	N

187

I, in (or id), din, dine, diner, ruined (or inured), untried.

188

1. *The Merchant of Venice*;
2. *The Two Gentlemen of Verona*;
3. *The Merry Wives of Windsor*.

189

Remember throughout that there are 3 different initials in each case (intro). Edward lives in either B or C (clue 1), as does David (clue 3), so Andy is in D (2) and Dina in E. If Christine is in B, then Edward is in C (1), David is in b and Beryl in C (3), leaving nowhere for Amy to live. So Christine is in A and Edward in B (1), David is in C and Beryl in D. Ella isn't married to Edward (intro), so David. Amy is in B. Christine's husband isn't Colin, so Bert. Colin is married to Dina.

Thus:

A - Bert - Christine;
B - Edward - Amy;
C - David - Ella;
D - Andy - Beryl;
E - Colin - Dina.

SOLUTIONS

190

The hidden
word is:
SHAMPOO

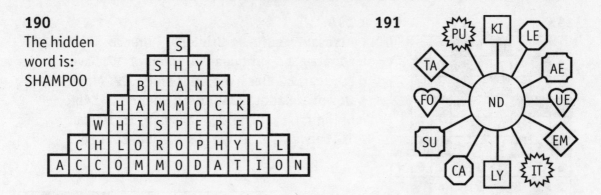

191

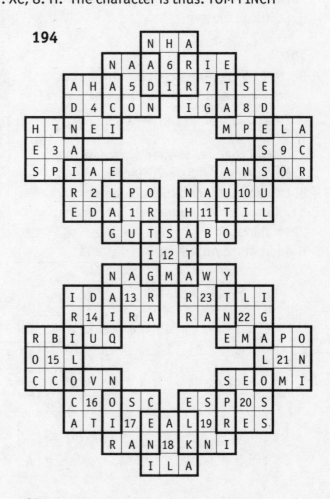

192

Novel in shaded
column:

Casino Royale
by Ian Fleming

C	A	M	P	H	O	R
A	V	E	R	A	G	E
S	H	A	M	B	L	E
I	M	P	E	T	U	S
N	I	G	H	T	I	E
O	P	T	I	M	U	M
R	O	T	A	T	E	S
O	F	F	I	C	E	R
Y	E	A	R	N	E	D
A	S	P	I	R	I	N
L	A	T	E	R	A	L
E	M	U	L	A	T	E

193

1. AccidenT, 2. BuffalO, 3. TandeM, 4. CheaP, 5. YetI,
6. TiN, 7. XC, 8. H. The character is thus: TOM PINCH

194

SOLUTIONS

195

1	3	2		1		1	3	1
9		4	3	2		0		3
6	0	0		7		8	6	4
			5	2	8		4	
4	3	2	0		4	5	8	5
	4		5	1	4			
6	5	5		0		2	6	4
2		2		2	1	6		2
5	4	4		4		5	4	0

198

1. Parcel, 2. Rapped, 3. Draper, 4. Polite, 5. Static, 6. Crater.

199

Butterfly F is different - it has 14 shapes on its wings and the others have 12.

200

1. Zeus, 2. Saliva, 3. Atlantic, 4. Calcium, 5. Mercury, 6. Yiddish, 7. Handel, 8. Labrador, 9. Rouble, 10. Equator, 11. Romania, 12. Aubergine, 13. Epsom, 14. Malaria.
Hidden word: ABSINTHE

196

Across: 7. Baffle, 8. Bridle, 9. Florence, 10. Itch, 11. Stay, 12. Fatigued, 14. Integral, 17. Save, 19. Scar, 20. Deserved, 21. Canine, 22. Alpine.
Down: 1. Ballot, 2. Affray, 3. Jennifer, 4. Able, 5. Hiding, 6. Cliché, 13. Talisman, 15. Nectar, 16. Earwig, 17. Scrape, 18. Vienna, 20. Deed.

197

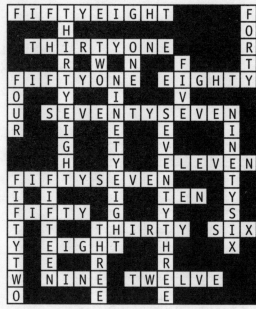

201

W	A	L	L	A	B	Y
P	A	N	T	H	E	R	N
R	A	C	C	O	O	N
L	E	M	M	I	N	G
B	U	F	F	A	L	O
H	A	M	S	T	E	R
M	U	S	T	A	N	G
G	I	R	A	F	F	E

SOLUTIONS

202

HA	ST	EN		SP	EE	CH		CI	CA	DA
GG		MI	NG	LE		AR	CA	NE		MP
LE	VI	TY		EN	GA	GE		MA	ID	EN
	RT			MB				EA		
SQ	UE	AL		SU	IT	OR		PU	LS	AR
UA		LE	AR	NT		AT	TE	ND		AB
RE	FU	GE		AN	CH	OR		IT	AL	IC
	MB			OI				CO		
PA	LE	ST		SE	CE	DE		IN	VE	ST
GO		RI	TU	AL		AL	UM	NA		IF
DA	TI	VE		ED	GI	ER		TE	MP	LE

203
Technologically.

204

A	C	C	B	B	A
C	B	A	A	C	B
B	A	C	C	B	A
C	B	B	A	A	C
A	A	B	B	C	C
B	C	A	C	A	B

205
Across: 1. Metre, 4. Enemy, 7. Ink,
8. Ahead, 9. Alike, 11. Dry, 12. Crow,
15. Ruin, 17. Obese, 18. Year, 19. Best,
22. Red, 24. Rural, 26. Drive, 27. Old,
28. Bonus, 29. Agree.
Down: 1. Mrahc, 2. Trevo, 3. Eid,
4. Ekar, 5. Eri, 6. Ydeen, 10. Lyreb,
11. Daerd, 13. Rae, 14. Worra, 16. Iks,
18. Yrreb, 20. Esiar, 21. Tcele, 23. Elos,
25. Ron, 26. Dda.

206

A	R	I	E	S		A		D
	O			N	A	I	V	E
A	U	D	I	O		S		A
	T			O		L		L
H	E	A	R	T	B	E	A	T
E		H		I			U	
A		E		E	L	U	D	E
V	I	A	L	S			I	
E		D		T	A	S	T	E

The word is ORATES.

207

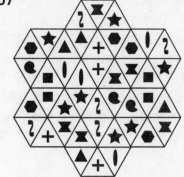

208
A, D, F, J, K and Q.

209

Every letter in the code stands for the one preceding it alphabetically, so that B=A, C=B, D=C, etc, until Z=Y; after which A=Z.

Thus:

The chief difficulty Alice found at first was in managing her flamingo: she succeeded in getting its body tucked away, comfortably enough, under her arm, with its legs hanging down, but generally, just as she had got its neck nicely straightened out, and was going to give the hedgehog a blow with its head, it WOULD twist itself round and look up in her face, with such a puzzled expression that she could not help bursting out laughing: and when she had got its head down, and was going to begin again, it was very provoking to find that the hedgehog had unrolled itself, and was in the act of crawling away: besides all this, there was generally a ridge or furrow in the way wherever she wanted to send the hedgehog to, and, as the doubled-up soldiers were always getting up and walking off to other parts of the ground, Alice soon came to the conclusion that it was a very difficult game indeed.

The players all played at once without waiting for turns, quarrelling all the while, and fighting for the hedgehogs; and in a very short time the Queen was in a furious passion, and went stamping about, and shouting "Off with his head!" or "Off with her head!" about once in a minute.

210

The name of SIR FRANCIS DRAKE can be found reading in the sixth vertical column from the left, starting in the third square down.

211

Across: 1. Outcome, 5. Codes, 8. Earlier, 9. Miser, 10. Stout, 11. Natural, 12. Shandy, 14. Satyrs, 17. Roaming, 19. Scald, 22. Image, 23. Ignored, 24. Exalt, 25. Tuesday.

Down: 1. Obeys, 2. Torso, 3. Omitted, 4. Errand, 5. Comet, 6. Destroy, 7. Surplus, 12. Sardine, 13. Alabama, 15. Absence, 16. Egoist, 18. Inert, 20. Acrid, 21. Daddy.

212

7	9	2	■	1	■	3	5	7
5	■	2	2	0	■	9	■	8
3	9	5	■	2	■	6	2	4
■	■	9	4	9	■	9	■	
5	8	1	7	■	4	1	5	5
■	3	■	2	5	1	■	■	
2	1	2	■	0	■	8	3	1
4	■	6	■	8	6	6	■	9
8	5	1	■	6	■	9	3	8

SOLUTIONS

213

Mrs Jones purchased pot H.

214

1. Carton, 2. Packet, 3. Option,
4. Monkey, 5. Myopia, 6. Trains.

215

S	E	A	L		D	I	N	O	S	A	U	R
E		L		E		N		U		I		A
R	E	L	A	X	E	D		T	A	R	R	Y
V		O		T		O		M		P		S
I	N	T	E	R	R	O	G	A	T	O	R	
C		A		R		N		R		R		B
E	V	O	L	V	E		D	O	C	T	O	R
D		P		A		A		E		O		I
	N	E	I	G	H	B	O	U	R	I	N	G
T		N		A		L		V		N		H
O	N	I	O	N		A	P	R	I	C	O	T
F		N		Z		Z		E		U		E
U	N	G	L	A	Z	E	D		G	R	I	N

217

Crete, Greece, Portugal, Spain,
Gibraltar, Australia, America, Italy,
Germany, Ireland, Scotland, Sweden,
Turkey, Thailand, India, Mexico,
Belgium, France, Japan, Austria,
Russia, Netherlands, Switzerland.

218

E

216

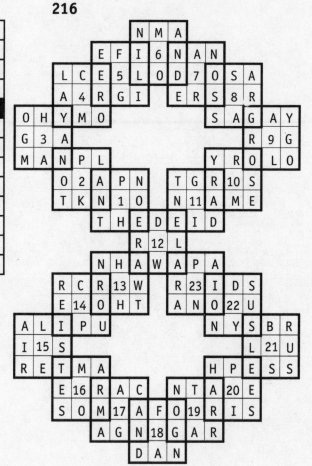